Learn, Practice, Succeed

Eureka Math®
Grade 7
Module 5

Published by Great Minds®

Copyright © 2019 Great Minds®.

Printed in the U.S.A.

This book may be purchased from the publisher at eureka-math.org.

4 5 6 7 8 9 10 LSC 26 25 24 23 22 21

ISBN 978-1-64054-976-0

G7-M5-LPS-05.2019

Students, families, and educators:

Thank you for being part of the *Eureka Math®* community, where we celebrate the joy, wonder, and thrill of mathematics.

In *Eureka Math* classrooms, learning is activated through rich experiences and dialogue. That new knowledge is best retained when it is reinforced with intentional practice. The *Learn, Practice, Succeed* book puts in students' hands the problem sets and fluency exercises they need to express and consolidate their classroom learning and master grade-level mathematics. Once students learn and practice, they know they can succeed.

What is in the Learn, Practice, Succeed *book?*

Fluency Practice: Our printed fluency activities utilize the format we call a Sprint. Instead of rote recall, Sprints use patterns across a sequence of problems to engage students in reasoning and to reinforce number sense while building speed and accuracy. Sprints are inherently differentiated, with problems building from simple to complex. The tempo of the Sprint provides a low-stakes adrenaline boost that increases memory and automaticity.

Classwork: A carefully sequenced set of examples, exercises, and reflection questions support students' in-class experiences and dialogue. Having classwork preprinted makes efficient use of class time and provides a written record that students can refer to later.

Exit Tickets: Students show teachers what they know through their work on the daily Exit Ticket. This check for understanding provides teachers with valuable real-time evidence of the efficacy of that day's instruction, giving critical insight into where to focus next.

Homework Helpers and Problem Sets: The daily Problem Set gives students additional and varied practice and can be used as differentiated practice or homework. A set of worked examples, Homework Helpers, support students' work on the Problem Set by illustrating the modeling and reasoning the curriculum uses to build understanding of the concepts the lesson addresses.

Homework Helpers and Problem Sets from prior grades or modules can be leveraged to build foundational skills. When coupled with *Affirm®*, *Eureka Math*'s digital assessment system, these Problem Sets enable educators to give targeted practice and to assess student progress. Alignment with the mathematical models and language used across *Eureka Math* ensures that students notice the connections and relevance to their daily instruction, whether they are working on foundational skills or getting extra practice on the current topic.

Where can I learn more about Eureka Math *resources?*

The Great Minds® team is committed to supporting students, families, and educators with an ever-growing library of resources, available at eureka-math.org. The website also offers inspiring stories of success in the *Eureka Math* community. Share your insights and accomplishments with fellow users by becoming a *Eureka Math* Champion.

Best wishes for a year filled with "aha" moments!

Jill Diniz

Jill Diniz
Chief Academic Officer, Mathematics
Great Minds

Contents

Module 5: Statistics and Probability

Have you ever heard a weather forecaster say there is a 40% chance of rain tomorrow or a football referee tell a team there is a 50/50 chance of getting a heads on a coin toss to determine which team starts the game? These are probability statements. In this lesson, you are going to investigate probability and how likely it is that some events will occur.

Example 1: Spinner Game

Suppose you and your friend are about to play a game using the spinner shown here:

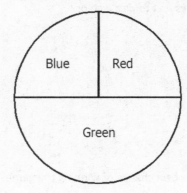

Rules of the game:

1. Decide who will go first.
2. Each person picks a color. Both players cannot pick the same color.
3. Each person takes a turn spinning the spinner and recording what color the spinner stops on. The winner is the person whose color is the first to happen 10 times.

Play the game, and remember to record the color the spinner stops on for each spin.

Lesson 1:   Chance Experiments

Exercises 1–4

1. Which color was the first to occur 10 times?

2. Do you think it makes a difference who goes first to pick a color?

3. Which color would you pick to give you the best chance of winning the game? Why would you pick that color?

4. Below are three different spinners. On which spinner is the green likely to win, unlikely to win, and equally likely to win?

Spinner A	Spinner B	Spinner C
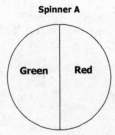	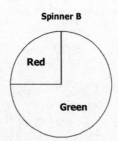	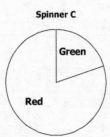

EUREKA MATH®

Example 2: What Is Probability?

Probability is a measure of how likely it is that an event will happen. A probability is indicated by a number between 0 and 1. Some events are certain to happen, while others are impossible. In most cases, the probability of an event happening is somewhere between certain and impossible.

For example, consider a bag that contains only red cubes. If you were to select one cube from the bag, you are certain to pick a red one. We say that an event that is certain to happen has a probability of 1. If we were to reach into the same bag of cubes, it is impossible to select a yellow cube. An impossible event has a probability of 0.

Description	Example	Explanation
Some events are *impossible*. These events have a probability of 0.	You have a bag with two green cubes, and you select one at random. Selecting a blue cube is an impossible event.	There is no way to select a blue cube if there are no blue cubes in the bag.
Some events are *certain*. These events have a probability of 1.	You have a bag with two green cubes, and you select one at random. Selecting a green cube is a certain event.	You will always get a green cube if there are only green cubes in the bag.
Some events are classified as *equally likely to occur or to not occur*. These events have a probability of $\frac{1}{2}$.	You have a bag with one blue cube and one red cube, and you randomly pick one. Selecting a blue cube is equally likely to occur or not to occur.	Since exactly half of the bag is made up of blue cubes and exactly half of the bag comprises red cubes, there is a 50/50 chance (equally likely) of selecting a blue cube and a 50/50 chance (equally likely) of NOT selecting a blue cube.
Some events are more likely to occur than not to occur. These events have a probability that is greater than 0.5. These events could be described as *likely* to occur.	If you have a bag that contains eight blue cubes and two red cubes and you select one at random, it is likely that you will get a blue cube.	Even though it is not certain that you will get a blue cube, a blue cube would be selected most of the time because there are many more blue cubes than red cubes.
Some events are less likely to occur than not to occur. These events have a probability that is less than 0.5. These events could be described as *unlikely* to occur.	If you have a bag that contains eight blue cubes and two red cubes and you select one at random, it is unlikely that you will get a red cube.	Even though it is not impossible to get a red cube, a red cube would not be selected very often because there are many more blue cubes than red cubes.

The figure below shows the probability scale.

Probability Scale

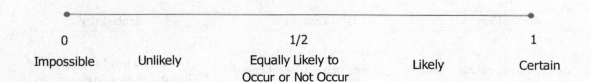

0		1/2		1
Impossible	Unlikely	Equally Likely to Occur or Not Occur	Likely	Certain

Exercises 5–10

5. Decide where each event would be located on the scale above. Place the letter for each event in the appropriate place on the probability scale.

    Event:

    A. You will see a live dinosaur on the way home from school today.

    B. A solid rock dropped in the water will sink.

    C. A round disk with one side red and the other side yellow will land yellow side up when flipped.

    D. A spinner with four equal parts numbered 1–4 will land on the 4 on the next spin.

    E. Your full name will be drawn when a full name is selected randomly from a bag containing the full names of all of the students in your class.

    F. A red cube will be drawn when a cube is selected from a bag that has five blue cubes and five red cubes.

    G. Tomorrow the temperature outside will be −250 degrees.

6. Design a spinner so that the probability of spinning a green is 1.

EUREKA MATH

7. Design a spinner so that the probability of spinning a green is 0.

8. Design a spinner with two outcomes in which it is equally likely to land on the red and green parts.

An event that is impossible has a probability of 0 and will never occur, no matter how many observations you make. This means that in a long sequence of observations, it will occur 0% of the time. An event that is certain has a probability of 1 and will always occur. This means that in a long sequence of observations, it will occur 100% of the time.

9. What do you think it means for an event to have a probability of $\frac{1}{2}$?

10. What do you think it means for an event to have a probability of $\frac{1}{4}$?

Lesson Summary

- *Probability* is a measure of how likely it is that an event will happen.

- A probability is a number between 0 and 1.

- The probability scale is as follows:

Probability Scale

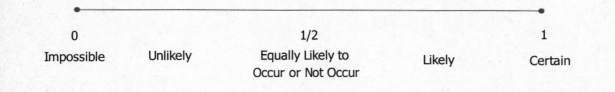

0	1/2	1
Impossible Unlikely	Equally Likely to Occur or Not Occur Likely	Certain

Lesson 1:   Chance Experiments

EUREKA
MATH

Name _____   Date _____

Decide where each of the following events would be located on the scale below. Place the letter for each event on the appropriate place on the probability scale.

PROBABILITY SCALE

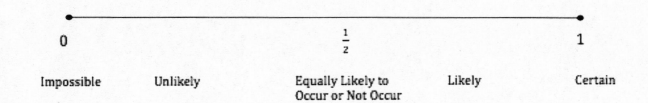

The numbers from 1 to 10 are written on small pieces of paper and placed in a bag. A piece of paper will be drawn from the bag.

    A. A piece of paper with a 5 is drawn from the bag.

    B. A piece of paper with an even number is drawn.

    C. A piece of paper with a 12 is drawn.

    D. A piece of paper with a number other than 1 is drawn.

    E. A piece of paper with a number divisible by 5 is drawn.

Probability Scale

The probability of an event will fall somewhere on the probability scale.

Probability Scale

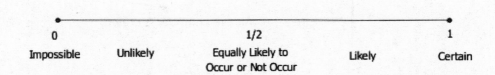

Decide whether each event is impossible, unlikely, equally likely, likely, or certain to occur.

1. It will start raining gum drops on the way home from school.

   Impossible

2. An even number will be chosen from a bag containing items numbered 1 through 20.

   Equally Likely

   > I know there are 20 numbers in the bag, and 10 of them are even. Therefore, the probability will be $\frac{10}{20}$, or $\frac{1}{2}$.

3. I will roll a composite number on a six-sided number cube with sides numbered 1 through 6.

   Unlikely

4. A letter chosen from the alphabet is a consonant.

   Likely

   > Twenty-one of the twenty-six letters in the alphabet are consonants, which means the probability is greater than half.

   > There are two composite numbers (4 and 6) on a six-sided number cube. That means two out of the six possible numbers are composite, making the probability less than half.

5. A number will be randomly drawn from the box shown below. Decide where each event would be located on the probability scale. Then, place the letter for each event on the appropriate location on the probability scale.

> There are 10 possible outcomes.

$$1 \quad 2 \quad 4 \quad 3$$
$$4 \quad$$
$$\quad 3 \quad 4$$
$$2 \quad$$
$$\quad 4 \quad 2$$

Event:

> Seven of the numbers are even.

A. An even number is drawn.

B. A 1 is drawn.

> All the outcomes are numbers.

C. A number is drawn.

> There are no letters.

D. A letter is drawn.

> Three appears twice, which means the event is unlikely. However, there are more possible outcomes for event E than for event B, which means event E should be to the right of event B, but event E is still unlikely.

E. A 3 is drawn.

PROBABILITY SCALE

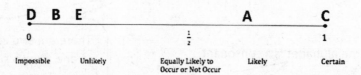

D	**B**	**E**		**A**		**C**
0			$\frac{1}{2}$			1
Impossible		Unlikely	Equally Likely to Occur or Not Occur	Likely		Certain

Lesson 1:   Chance Experiments

EUREKA MATH®

1. Match each spinner below with the words *impossible, unlikely, equally likely to occur or not occur, likely,* and *certain* to describe the chance of the spinner landing on black.

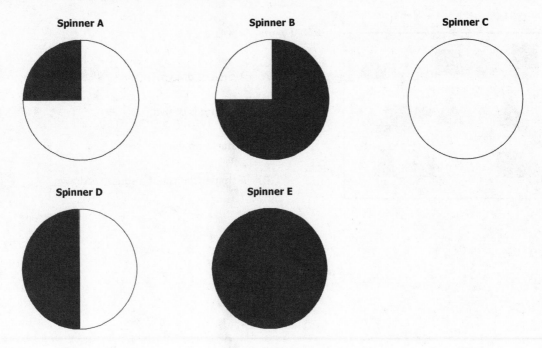

2. Decide if each of the following events is *impossible, unlikely, equally likely to occur or not occur, likely,* or *certain* to occur.

   a. A vowel will be picked when a letter is randomly selected from the word *lieu*.

   b. A vowel will be picked when a letter is randomly selected from the word *math*.

   c. A blue cube will be drawn from a bag containing only five blue and five black cubes.

   d. A red cube will be drawn from a bag of 100 red cubes.

   e. A red cube will be drawn from a bag of 10 red and 90 blue cubes.

3. A shape will be randomly drawn from the box shown below. Decide where each event would be located on the probability scale. Then, place the letter for each event on the appropriate place on the probability scale.

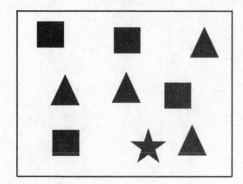

Event:

A. A circle is drawn.

B. A square is drawn.

C. A star is drawn.

D. A shape that is not a square is drawn.

Probability Scale

0	1/2		1
Impossible	Unlikely	Equally Likely to Occur or Not Occur	Likely	Certain

4. Color the squares below so that it would be equally likely to choose a blue or yellow square.

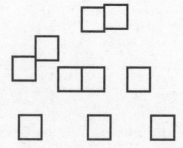

Lesson 1:   Chance Experiments

EUREKA MATH®

5. Color the squares below so that it would be likely but not certain to choose a blue square from the bag.

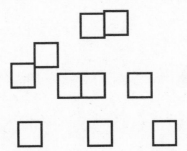

6. Color the squares below so that it would be unlikely but not impossible to choose a blue square from the bag.

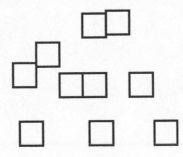

7. Color the squares below so that it would be impossible to choose a blue square from the bag.

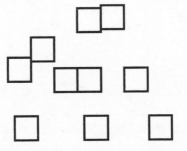

Exercises 1–8: Carnival Game

At the school carnival, there is a game in which students spin a large spinner. The spinner has four equal sections numbered 1–4 as shown below. To play the game, a student spins the spinner twice and adds the two numbers that the spinner lands on. If the sum is greater than or equal to 5, the student wins a prize.

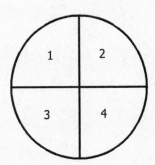

Play this game with your partner 15 times. Record the outcome of each spin in the table below.

Turn	First Spin Results	Second Spin Results	Sum
1			
2			
3			
4			
5			
6			
7			
8			
9			
10			
11			
12			
13			
14			
15			

1. Out of the 15 turns, how many times was the sum greater than or equal to 5?

2. What sum occurred most often?

3. What sum occurred least often?

4. If students were to play a lot of games, what fraction of the games would they win? Explain your answer.

5. Name a sum that would be impossible to get while playing the game.

6. What event is certain to occur while playing the game?

When you were spinning the spinner and recording the outcomes, you were performing a *chance experiment*. You can use the results from a chance experiment to estimate the probability of an event. In Exercise 1, you spun the spinner 15 times and counted how many times the sum was greater than or equal to 5. An estimate for the probability of a sum greater than or equal to 5 is

$$P(\text{sum} \geq 5) = \frac{\text{Number of observed occurrences of the event}}{\text{Total number of observations}}.$$

7. Based on your experiment of playing the game, what is your estimate for the probability of getting a sum of 5 or more?

8. Based on your experiment of playing the game, what is your estimate for the probability of getting a sum of exactly 5?

Example: Animal Crackers

A student brought a very large jar of animal crackers to share with students in class. Rather than count and sort all the different types of crackers, the student randomly chose 20 crackers and found the following counts for the different types of animal crackers. Estimate the probability of selecting a zebra.

Animal	Number Selected
Lion	2
Camel	1
Monkey	4
Elephant	5
Zebra	3
Penguin	3
Tortoise	2
	Total 20

Lesson 2:   Estimating Probabilities by Collecting Data   17

Exercises 9–15

If a student randomly selected a cracker from a large jar:

9. What is your estimate for the probability of selecting a lion?

10. What is your estimate for the probability of selecting a monkey?

11. What is your estimate for the probability of selecting a penguin or a camel?

12. What is your estimate for the probability of selecting a rabbit?

13. Is there the same number of each kind of animal cracker in the jar? Explain your answer.

14. If the student randomly selected another 20 animal crackers, would the same results occur? Why or why not?

15. If there are 500 animal crackers in the jar, how many elephants are in the jar? Explain your answer.

Lesson Summary

An estimate for finding the probability of an event occurring is

$$P(\text{event occurring}) = \frac{\text{Number of observed occurrences of the event}}{\text{Total number of observations}}.$$

Name _____   Date _____

In the following problems, round all of your decimal answers to three decimal places. Round all of your percents to the nearest tenth of a percent.

A student randomly selected crayons from a large bag of crayons. The table below shows the number of each color crayon in a bag. Now, suppose the student were to randomly select one crayon from the bag.

Color	Number
Brown	10
Blue	5
Yellow	3
Green	3
Orange	3
Red	6

1. What is the estimate for the probability of selecting a blue crayon from the bag? Express your answer as a fraction, decimal, or percent.

2. What is the estimate for the probability of selecting a brown crayon from the bag?

3. What is the estimate for the probability of selecting a red crayon *or* a yellow crayon from the bag?

4. What is the estimate for the probability of selecting a pink crayon from the bag?

5. Which color is most likely to be selected?

6. If there are 300 crayons in the bag, how many red crayons would you estimate are in the bag? Justify your answer.

Cole is eating candy from a bag that consists of different-colored pieces. Cole randomly picked pieces from the bag and recorded the number of each color in the table below.

Color	Number
Red	4
Brown	7
Green	4
Yellow	10
Blue	7
Orange	8

a. How many pieces of candy are in the bag?

40

> I add the number of each color of candy together to find the total amount of candy.

b. How many pieces of candy are yellow?

10

If Cole randomly selected a piece of candy from the bag:

c. What is the estimated probability of Cole eating an orange piece of candy?

$$\frac{8}{40} = \frac{1}{5} = 20\%$$

> The number of observed occurrences is 8, and the total number of observations is 40.

d. What is the estimated probability Cole will eat either a brown or blue piece of candy?

$$\frac{14}{40} = \frac{7}{20} = 35\%$$

> The number of observed occurrences is 14 because there are 7 brown pieces of candy and 7 blue pieces of candy in the bag.

e. If the bag of candy has 600 pieces of candy, how many pieces would you expect to be red?

$$\frac{4}{40} = \frac{1}{10} = 10\%$$

An estimate for the number of red pieces of candy would be 60 because 10% of 600 is 60.

I find the estimated probability of choosing a red piece of candy. I can use this percentage to estimate the total number of red pieces of candy in the bag.

EUREKA MATH

1. Play a game using the two spinners below. Spin each spinner once, and then multiply the outcomes together. If the result is less than or equal to 8, you win the game. Play the game 15 times, and record your results in the table below. Then, answer the questions that follow.

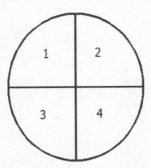
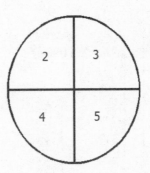

Turn	First Spin Results	Second Spin Results	Product
1			
2			
3			
4			
5			
6			
7			
8			
9			
10			
11			
12			
13			
14			
15			

a. What is your estimate for the probability of getting a product of 8 or less?

b. What is your estimate for the probability of getting a product of more than 8?

c. What is your estimate for the probability of getting a product of exactly 8?

d. What is the most likely product for this game?

e. If you play this game another 15 times, will you get the exact same results? Explain.

2. A seventh-grade student surveyed students at her school. She asked them to name their favorite pets. Below is a bar graph showing the results of the survey.

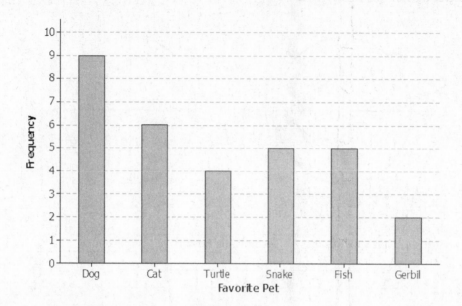

Use the results from the survey to answer the following questions.

a. How many students answered the survey question?

b. How many students said that a snake was their favorite pet?

Now, suppose a student is randomly selected and asked what his favorite pet is.

c. What is your estimate for the probability of that student saying that a dog is his favorite pet?

d. What is your estimate for the probability of that student saying that a gerbil is his favorite pet?

e. What is your estimate for the probability of that student saying that a frog is his favorite pet?

Lesson 2:   Estimating Probabilities by Collecting Data

EUREKA MATH®

3. A seventh-grade student surveyed 25 students at her school. She asked them how many hours a week they spend playing a sport or game outdoors. The results are listed in the table below.

Number of Hours	Tally	Frequency
0	| | |	3
1	| | | |	4
2	⫲⫲	5
3	⫲⫲ | |	7
4	| | |	3
5		0
6	| |	2
7		0
8	|	1

a. Draw a dot plot of the results.

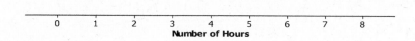

Suppose a student will be randomly selected.

b. What is your estimate for the probability of that student answering 3 hours?

c. What is your estimate for the probability of that student answering 8 hours?

d. What is your estimate for the probability of that student answering 6 or more hours?

e. What is your estimate for the probability of that student answering 3 or fewer hours?

f. If another 25 students were surveyed, do you think they would give the exact same results? Explain your answer.

g. If there are 200 students at the school, what is your estimate for the number of students who would say they play a sport or game outdoors 3 hours per week? Explain your answer.

4. A student played a game using one of the spinners below. The table shows the results of 15 spins. Which spinner did the student use? Give a reason for your answer.

Spin	Results
1	1
2	1
3	2
4	3
5	1
6	2
7	3
8	2
9	2
10	1
11	2
12	2
13	1
14	3
15	1

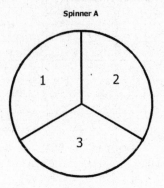

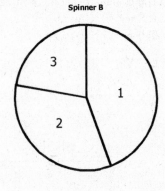

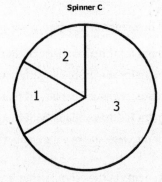

Lesson 2:   Estimating Probabilities by Collecting Data

EUREKA
MATH®

Exercises 1–6

Jamal, a seventh grader, wants to design a game that involves tossing paper cups. Jamal tosses a paper cup five times and records the outcome of each toss. An *outcome* is the result of a single trial of an experiment.

Here are the results of each toss:

Jamal noted that the paper cup could land in one of three ways: on its side, right side up, or upside down. The collection of these three outcomes is called the *sample space* of the experiment. The *sample space* of an experiment is the set of all possible outcomes of that experiment.

For example, the sample space when flipping a coin is heads, tails.

The sample space when drawing a colored cube from a bag that has 3 red, 2 blue, 1 yellow, and 4 green cubes is red, blue, yellow, green.

For each of the following chance experiments, list the sample space (i.e., all the possible outcomes).

1. Drawing a colored cube from a bag with 2 green, 1 red, 10 blue, and 3 black

2. Tossing an empty soup can to see how it lands

3. Shooting a free throw in a basketball game

4. Rolling a number cube with the numbers 1–6 on its faces

5. Selecting a letter from the word *probability*

6. Spinning the spinner:

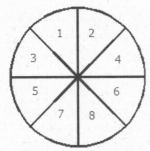

EUREKA
MATH

Example 2: Equally Likely Outcomes

The sample space for the paper cup toss was on its side, right side up, and upside down.

The outcomes of an experiment are equally likely to occur when the probability of each outcome is equal.

Toss the paper cup 30 times, and record in a table the results of each toss.

Toss	Outcome
1	
2	
3	
4	
5	
6	
7	
8	
9	
10	
11	
12	
13	
14	
15	
16	
17	
18	
19	
20	
21	
22	
23	
24	
25	
26	
27	
28	
29	
30	

Exercises 7–12

7. Using the results of your experiment, what is your estimate for the probability of a paper cup landing on its side?

8. Using the results of your experiment, what is your estimate for the probability of a paper cup landing upside down?

9. Using the results of your experiment, what is your estimate for the probability of a paper cup landing right side up?

10. Based on your results, do you think the three outcomes are equally likely to occur?

11. Using the spinner below, answer the following questions.

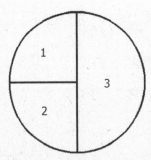

   a. Are the events spinning and landing on 1 or 2 equally likely?

Lesson 3:   Chance Experiments with Equally Likely Outcomes

EUREKA MATH

b.   Are the events spinning and landing on 2 or 3 equally likely?

c.   How many times do you predict the spinner will land on each section after 100 spins?

12. Draw a spinner that has 3 sections that are equally likely to occur when the spinner is spun. How many times do you
     think the spinner will land on each section after 100 spins?

Lesson Summary

An *outcome* is the result of a single observation of an experiment.

The *sample space* of an experiment is the set of all possible outcomes of that experiment.

The outcomes of an experiment are *equally likely* to occur when the probability of each outcome is equal.

Suppose a bag of crayons contains 10 green, 10 red, 10 yellow, 10 orange, and 10 purple crayons. If one crayon is selected from the bag and the color is noted, the *outcome* is the color that is chosen. The *sample space* will be the colors: green, red, yellow, orange, and purple. Each color is *equally likely* to be selected because each color has the same chance of being chosen.

EUREKA MATH

Name _____ Date _____

The numbers 1–10 are written on note cards and placed in a bag. One card will be drawn from the bag at random.

1. List the sample space for this experiment.

2. Are the events selecting an even number and selecting an odd number equally likely? Explain your answer.

3. Are the events selecting a number divisible by 3 and selecting a number divisible by 5 equally likely?
    Explain your answer.

The sample space is all the possible outcomes.

For each of the following chance experiments, list the sample space.

1. Selecting a marble from a bag of 6 green marbles, 8 yellow marbles, and 4 red marbles

    Green, yellow, and red

    When listing the sample space, I list all the letters in the word *homework*. However, the letter *o* only needs to be listed once.

2. Selecting a letter from the word *homework*

    h, o, m, e, w, r, and k

3. Spinning the spinner below

    1, 2, and 3

    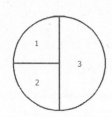

    It does not matter if the outcomes are equally likely; the sample space just focuses on the possible outcomes.

For each of the following problems, decide if the two outcomes listed are equally likely to occur. Give a reason for your answer.

The letters *i* and *b* both occur twice in the word *probability*.

4. Selecting the letters *i* or *b* from the word *probability*

    Yes, both i and b occur the same number of times in the word probability.

5. Selecting a red or blue uniform shirt when Lincoln has 4 red uniform shirts and 5 blue uniform shirts

    No, Lincoln has a slightly higher chance of picking a blue shirt.

    Lincoln has a different number of each color shirt, which means each outcome is not equally likely.

6. Landing on blue or green on the spinner below

    No, it is more likely to land on green than on blue.

    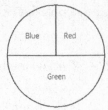

    The area of green on the spinner is larger than the area of blue. Therefore, the outcomes are not equally likely.

1. For each of the following chance experiments, list the sample space (all the possible outcomes).

   a. Rolling a 4-sided die with the numbers 1–4 on the faces of the die

   b. Selecting a letter from the word *mathematics*

   c. Selecting a marble from a bag containing 50 black marbles and 45 orange marbles

   d. Selecting a number from the even numbers 2–14, including 2 and 14

   e. Spinning the spinner below:

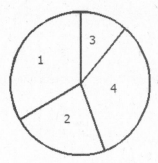

2. For each of the following, decide if the two outcomes listed are equally likely to occur. Give a reason for your answer.

   a. Rolling a 1 or a 2 when a 6-sided number cube with the numbers 1–6 on the faces of the cube is rolled

   b. Selecting the letter *a* or *k* from the word *take*

   c. Selecting a black or an orange marble from a bag containing 50 black and 45 orange marbles

   d. Selecting a 4 or an 8 from the even numbers 2–14, including 2 and 14

   e. Landing on a 1 or a 3 when spinning the spinner below

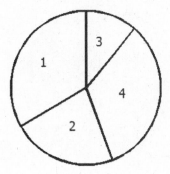

3. Color the squares below so that it would be equally likely to choose a blue or yellow square.

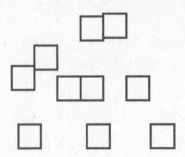

4. Color the squares below so that it would be more likely to choose a blue than a yellow square.

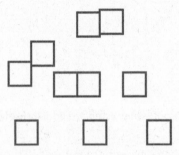

5. You are playing a game using the spinner below. The game requires that you spin the spinner twice. For example, one outcome could be yellow on the 1st spin and red on the 2nd spin. List the sample space (all the possible outcomes) for the two spins.

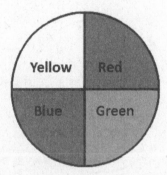

6. List the sample space for the chance experiment of flipping a coin twice.

Examples: Theoretical Probability

In a previous lesson, you saw that to find an estimate of the probability of an event for a chance experiment you divide

$$P(\text{event}) = \frac{\text{Number of observed occurrences of the event}}{\text{Total number of observations}}.$$

Your teacher has a bag with some cubes colored yellow, green, blue, and red. The cubes are identical except for their color. Your teacher will conduct a chance experiment by randomly drawing a cube with replacement from the bag. Record the outcome of each draw in the table below.

Trial	Outcome
1	
2	
3	
4	
5	
6	
7	
8	
9	
10	
11	
12	
13	
14	
15	
16	
17	
18	
19	
20	

1. Based on the 20 trials, estimate for the probability of

    a. Choosing a yellow cube

    b. Choosing a green cube

    c. Choosing a red cube

    d. Choosing a blue cube

2. If there are 40 cubes in the bag, how many cubes of each color are in the bag? Explain.

3. If your teacher were to randomly draw another 20 cubes one at a time and with replacement from the bag, would you see exactly the same results? Explain.

Lesson 4:   Calculating Probabilities for Chance Experiments
                                     with Equally Likely Outcomes

EUREKA
MATH

4. Find the fraction of each color of cubes in the bag.

    Yellow

    Green

    Red

    Blue

Each fraction is the *theoretical probability* of choosing a particular color of cube when a cube is randomly drawn from the bag.

When all the possible outcomes of an experiment are equally likely, the probability of each outcome is

$$P(\text{outcome}) = \frac{1}{\text{Number of possible outcomes}}.$$

An event is a collection of outcomes, and when the outcomes are equally likely, the theoretical probability of an event can be expressed as

$$P(\text{event}) = \frac{\text{Number of favorable outcomes}}{\text{Number of possible outcomes}}.$$

The theoretical probability of drawing a blue cube is

$$P(\text{blue}) = \frac{\text{Number of blue cubes}}{\text{Total number of cubes}} = \frac{10}{40}.$$

5. Is each color equally likely to be chosen? Explain your answer.

6. How do the theoretical probabilities of choosing each color from Exercise 4 compare to the experimental probabilities you found in Exercise 1?

7. An experiment consisted of flipping a nickel and a dime. The first step in finding the theoretical probability of obtaining a heads on the nickel and a heads on the dime is to list the sample space. For this experiment, complete the sample space below.

Nickel   Dime

What is the probability of flipping two heads?

Exercises 1–4

1. Consider a chance experiment of rolling a six-sided number cube with the numbers 1–6 on the faces.
    a. What is the sample space? List the probability of each outcome in the sample space.

    b. What is the probability of rolling an odd number?

    c. What is the probability of rolling a number less than 5?

Lesson 4:   Calculating Probabilities for Chance Experiments
                              with Equally Likely Outcomes

EUREKA
MATH

2. Consider an experiment of randomly selecting a letter from the word *number*.

    a. What is the sample space? List the probability of each outcome in the sample space.

    b. What is the probability of selecting a vowel?

    c. What is the probability of selecting the letter *z*?

3. Consider an experiment of randomly selecting a square from a bag of 10 squares.

    a. Color the squares below so that the probability of selecting a blue square is $\frac{1}{2}$.

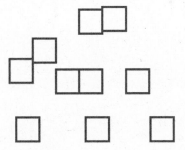

b.   Color the squares below so that the probability of selecting a blue square is $\frac{4}{5}$.

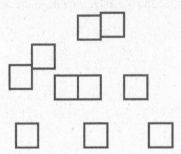

4.   Students are playing a game that requires spinning the two spinners shown below. A student wins the game if both spins land on red. What is the probability of winning the game? Remember to first list the sample space and the probability of each outcome in the sample space. There are eight possible outcomes to this chance experiment.

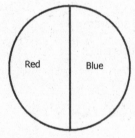

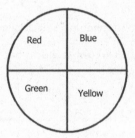

EUREKA
MATH®

Lesson Summary

When all the possible outcomes of an experiment are equally likely, the probability of each outcome is

$$P(\text{outcome}) = \frac{1}{\text{Number of possible outcomes}}.$$

An event is a collection of outcomes, and when all outcomes are equally likely, the theoretical probability of an event can be expressed as

$$P(\text{event}) = \frac{\text{Number of favorable outcomes}}{\text{Number of possible outcomes}}.$$

Name _____   Date _____

An experiment consists of randomly drawing a cube from a bag containing three red and two blue cubes.

1. What is the sample space of this experiment?

2. List the probability of each outcome in the sample space.

3. Is the probability of selecting a red cube equal to the probability of selecting a blue cube? Explain.

Lesson 4:   Calculating Probabilities for Chance Experiments   49
                with Equally Likely Outcomes

Calculate the Probability of Events when Outcomes are Not Equally Likely

1. In a middle school orchestra, there are 6 sixth graders, 11 seventh graders, and 8 eighth graders.

> There are 25 students in the orchestra because $6 + 11 + 8 = 25$. I know this represents the number of possible outcomes.

a. If one student is randomly chosen to complete a solo, what is the probability that a seventh grader is chosen?

$$\frac{11}{25}$$

> The number of favorable outcomes is the number of seventh graders in the orchestra.

b. If one student is randomly chosen, is it equally likely to pick a sixth, seventh, or eighth grader? Explain.

No, there are not the same number of sixth, seventh, or eighth graders.

> In order for outcomes to be equally likely, the number of favorable outcomes must be the same.

Calculate the Probability of Events with Equally Likely Outcomes

2. Use the spinner to the right to answer the following questions.

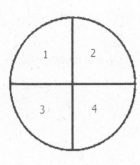

a. What is the probability of landing on an even number?

$$\frac{2}{4} = \frac{1}{2}$$

> There are two even numbers (2 and 4) on the spinner.

> There are 4 possible outcomes because there are 4 sections on the spinner.

b. What is the probability of landing on a composite number?

$\frac{1}{4}$

> There is only one composite number, 4, on the spinner.

c. Is landing on each section of the spinner equally likely to occur? Explain.

Yes, each section has the same area.

3. A chance experiment consists of rolling a number cube with the numbers 1–6 on the faces of the cube and flipping a coin.

a. List the sample space of this chance experiment. List the probability of each outcome in the sample space.

Sample Space: 1T, 1H, 2T, 2H, 3T, 3H, 4T, 4H, 5T, 5H, 6T, 6H

The probability of each outcome is $\frac{1}{12}$.

> There are 12 possible outcomes, and they are all equally likely to occur.

b. What is the probability of getting the number 5 on the number cube and a tails on the coin?

$\frac{1}{12}$

> It is estimated that this outcome will occur once in 12 trials.

c. What is the probability of getting a heads on the coin and an odd number on the number cube?

$\frac{3}{12}$, *or* $\frac{1}{4}$

> It is estimated that this outcome will occur three times in 12 trials.

EUREKA
MATH

1. In a seventh-grade class of 28 students, there are 16 girls and 12 boys. If one student is randomly chosen to win a prize, what is the probability that a girl is chosen?

2. An experiment consists of spinning the spinner once.
   a. Find the probability of landing on a 2.
   b. Find the probability of landing on a 1.
   c. Is landing in each section of the spinner equally likely to occur? Explain.

   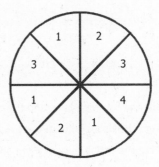

3. An experiment consists of randomly picking a square section from the board shown below.
   a. Find the probability of choosing a triangle.
   b. Find the probability of choosing a star.
   c. Find the probability of choosing an empty square.
   d. Find the probability of choosing a circle.

   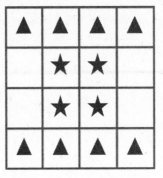

4. Seventh graders are playing a game where they randomly select two integers 0–9, inclusive, to form a two-digit number. The same integer might be selected twice.
   a. List the sample space for this chance experiment. List the probability of each outcome in the sample space.
   b. What is the probability that the number formed is between 90 and 99, inclusive?
   c. What is the probability that the number formed is evenly divisible by 5?
   d. What is the probability that the number formed is a factor of 64?

5. A chance experiment consists of flipping a coin and rolling a number cube with the numbers 1–6 on the faces of the cube.
   a. List the sample space of this chance experiment. List the probability of each outcome in the sample space.
   b. What is the probability of getting a heads on the coin and the number 3 on the number cube?
   c. What is the probability of getting a tails on the coin and an even number on the number cube?

6. A chance experiment consists of spinning the two spinners below.

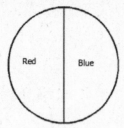   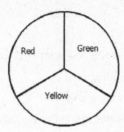

a. List the sample space and the probability of each outcome.

b. Find the probability of the event of getting a red on the first spinner and a red on the second spinner.

c. Find the probability of a red on at least one of the spinners.

Lesson 4:   Calculating Probabilities for Chance Experiments
with Equally Likely Outcomes

EUREKA
MATH

In previous lessons, you learned that when the outcomes in a sample space are equally likely, the probability of an event is the number of outcomes in the event divided by the number of outcomes in the sample space. However, when the outcomes in the sample space are *not* equally likely, we need to take a different approach.

Example 1

When Jenna goes to the farmers' market, she usually buys bananas. The number of bananas she might buy and their probabilities are shown in the table below.

Number of Bananas	0	1	2	3	4	5
Probability	0.1	0.1	0.1	0.2	0.2	0.3

a. What is the probability that Jenna buys exactly 3 bananas?

b. What is the probability that Jenna does not buy any bananas?

c. What is the probability that Jenna buys more than 3 bananas?

d. What is the probability that Jenna buys at least 3 bananas?

e. What is the probability that Jenna does not buy exactly 3 bananas?

Notice that the sum of the probabilities in the table is one whole ($0.1 + 0.1 + 0.1 + 0.2 + 0.2 + 0.3 = 1$). This is always true; when we add up the probabilities of all the possible outcomes, the result is always 1. So, taking 1 and subtracting the probability of the event gives us the probability of something *not* occurring.

Exercises 1–2

Jenna's husband, Rick, is concerned about his diet. On any given day, he eats 0, 1, 2, 3, or 4 servings of fruits and vegetables. The probabilities are given in the table below.

Number of Servings of Fruits and Vegetables	0	1	2	3	4
Probability	0.08	0.13	0.28	0.39	0.12

1. On a given day, find the probability that Rick eats

    a. Two servings of fruits and vegetables

    b. More than two servings of fruits and vegetables

    c. At least two servings of fruits and vegetables

2. Find the probability that Rick does not eat exactly two servings of fruits and vegetables.

Example 2

Luis works in an office, and the phone rings occasionally. The possible number of phone calls he receives in an afternoon and their probabilities are given in the table below.

Number of Phone Calls	0	1	2	3	4
Probability	$\frac{1}{6}$	$\frac{1}{6}$	$\frac{2}{9}$	$\frac{1}{3}$	$\frac{1}{9}$

    a. Find the probability that Luis receives 3 or 4 phone calls.

EUREKA MATH

b. Find the probability that Luis receives fewer than 2 phone calls.

c. Find the probability that Luis receives 2 or fewer phone calls.

d. Find the probability that Luis does not receive 4 phone calls.

Exercises 3–7

When Jenna goes to the farmers' market, she also usually buys some broccoli. The possible number of heads of broccoli that she buys and the probabilities are given in the table below.

Number of Heads of Broccoli	0	1	2	3	4
Probability	$\frac{1}{12}$	$\frac{1}{6}$	$\frac{5}{12}$	$\frac{1}{4}$	$\frac{1}{12}$

3. Find the probability that Jenna:

   a. Buys exactly 3 heads of broccoli

   b. Does not buy exactly 3 heads of broccoli

   c. Buys more than 1 head of broccoli

   d. Buys at least 3 heads of broccoli

The diagram below shows a spinner designed like the face of a clock. The sectors of the spinner are colored red (R), blue (B), green (G), and yellow (Y).

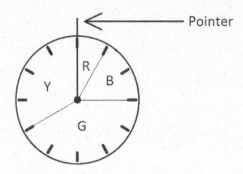

Pointer

4. Writing your answers as fractions in lowest terms, find the probability that the pointer stops on the following colors.
   a. Red:

   b. Blue:

   c. Green:

   d. Yellow:

5. Complete the table of probabilities below.

Color	Red	Blue	Green	Yellow
Probability				

Lesson 5:   Chance Experiments with Outcomes That Are
Not Equally Likely

EUREKA
MATH

6. Find the probability that the pointer stops in either the blue region or the green region.

7. Find the probability that the pointer does not stop in the green region.

Lesson Summary

In a probability experiment where the outcomes are not known to be equally likely, the formula for the probability of an event does not necessarily apply:

$$P(\text{event}) = \frac{\text{Number of outcomes in the event}}{\text{Number of outcomes in the sample space}}.$$

For example:

- To find the probability that the score is greater than 3, add the probabilities of all the scores that are greater than 3.

- To find the probability of not getting a score of 3, calculate $1 -$ (the probability of getting a 3).

EUREKA
MATH

Name _____   Date _____

Carol is sitting on the bus on the way home from school and is thinking about the fact that she has three homework assignments to do tonight. The table below shows her estimated probabilities of completing 0, 1, 2, or all 3 of the assignments.

Number of Homework Assignments Completed	0	1	2	3
Probability	$\frac{1}{6}$	$\frac{2}{9}$	$\frac{5}{18}$	$\frac{1}{3}$

1. Writing your answers as fractions in lowest terms, find the probability that Carol completes
   a. Exactly one assignment

   b. More than one assignment

   c. At least one assignment

2. Find the probability that the number of homework assignments Carol completes is not exactly 2.

3. Carol has a bag containing 3 red chips, 10 blue chips, and 7 green chips. Estimate the probability (as a fraction or decimal) of Carol reaching into her bag and pulling out a green chip.

1. Charlie is training for a race and is supposed to run every day during the week. The table below shows the estimated probabilities of running 1, 2, 3, 4, 5, 6, or 7 days a week.

Number of Days	1	2	3	4	5	6	7
Probability	0.1	0.1	0.1	0.2	0.3	0.2	0

Find the probability that Charlie will

> In order to find the probability of an event, I add the probability of each of the desired outcomes together.

a. Run more than 4 days during the week.

> "More than 4 days" means that Charlie will run 5, 6, or 7 days.

$$0.3 + 0.2 + 0 = 0.5$$

The probability that Charlie will run more than 4 days a week is 0.5.

> "At most 3 days" means that Charlie will run 3 or fewer days.

b. Run at most 3 days.

$$0.1 + 0.1 + 0.1 = 0.3$$

The probability that Charlie will run at most 3 days is 0.3.

c. Not run exactly 1 day.

    Method 1:

    $$0.1 + 0.1 + 0.2 + 0.3 + 0.2 + 0 = 0.9$$

    Method 2:

    $$1 - 0.1 = 0.9$$

    The probability that Charlie will not run exactly 1 day is 0.9.

> I can solve this problem two ways:
> 1. I can find the sum of all the probabilities, except for the probability of running 1 day.
> 2. The total probability is 1, so I can subtract $1 - P(1)$.

2. Sarah surveyed her friends to determine the number of pets each friend has. The survey results are shown in the table below.

Number of Pets	0	1	2	3	4
Number of Friends	8	6	3	1	2

a. How many friends did Sarah survey?

$8 + 6 + 3 + 1 + 2 = 20$

Sarah surveyed 20 friends.

b. What is the probability that a randomly selected friend does not have any pets? Write your answer as a fraction in lowest terms.

$\frac{8}{20} = \frac{2}{5}$

> The 8 represents the number of friends who have zero pets, and the 20 represents the total number of friends surveyed.

The probability that Sarah will select a friend who does not have any pets is $\frac{2}{5}$.

c. The table below shows the possible number of pets and the probabilities of each number of pets. Complete the table by writing the probabilities as fractions in lowest terms.

Number of Pets	0	1	2	3	1
Probability	$\frac{8}{20} = \frac{2}{5}$	$\frac{6}{20} = \frac{3}{10}$	$\frac{3}{20}$	$\frac{1}{20}$	$\frac{2}{20} = \frac{1}{10}$

> To find each probability, I put the number of favorable outcomes in the numerator and the total number of outcomes in the denominator. If possible, I simplify the fraction.

Lesson 5:   Chance Experiments with Outcomes That Are
                              Not Equally Likely

EUREKA MATH

d. Writing your answers as fractions in lowest terms, find the probability that the student:

    i.   Has fewer than 3 pets.

$$\frac{2}{5} + \frac{3}{10} + \frac{3}{20}$$

$$\frac{8}{20} + \frac{6}{20} + \frac{3}{20}$$

$$\frac{17}{20}$$

> In order to add the probabilities of a friend having 0, 1, or 2 pets, I find a common denominator or use the fractions that are not simplified from the table.

    ii. Does not have exactly 4 pets.

> The total probability is 1, so I would subtract the probability of a friend having four pets from 1.

$$1 - \frac{1}{10}$$

$$\frac{10}{10} - \frac{1}{10}$$

$$\frac{9}{10}$$

> $\frac{10}{10}$ represents the same value as 1.

> NOTE: I could also add the probabilities of a friend having 0, 1, 2, or 3 pets together to get the probability of not having 4 pets.

1. The Gator Girls is a soccer team. The possible number of goals the Gator Girls will score in a game and their probabilities are shown in the table below.

Number of Goals	0	1	2	3	4
Probability	0.22	0.31	0.33	0.11	0.03

Find the probability that the Gator Girls:

a. Score more than two goals

b. Score at least two goals

c. Do not score exactly 3 goals

2. The diagram below shows a spinner. The pointer is spun, and the player is awarded a prize according to the color on which the pointer stops.

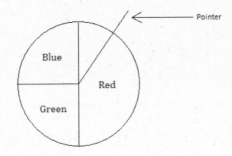

a. What is the probability that the pointer stops in the red region?

b. Complete the table below showing the probabilities of the three possible results.

Color	Red	Green	Blue
Probability			

c. Find the probability that the pointer stops on green or blue.

d. Find the probability that the pointer does not stop on green.

3. Wayne asked every student in his class how many siblings (brothers and sisters) they had. The survey results are shown in the table below. (Wayne included himself in the results.)

Number of Siblings	0	1	2	3	4
Number of Students	4	5	14	6	3

(Note: The table tells us that 4 students had no siblings, 5 students had one sibling, 14 students had two siblings, and so on.)

a. How many students are there in Wayne's class, including Wayne?

b. What is the probability that a randomly selected student does not have any siblings? Write your answer as a fraction in lowest terms.

c. The table below shows the possible number of siblings and the probabilities of each number. Complete the table by writing the probabilities as fractions in lowest terms.

Number of Siblings	0	1	2	3	4
Probability					

d. Writing your answers as fractions in lowest terms, find the probability that the student:

    i.   Has fewer than two siblings

    ii. Has two or fewer siblings

    iii. Does not have exactly one sibling

EUREKA MATH®

Suppose a girl attends a preschool where the students are studying primary colors. To help teach calendar skills, the teacher has each student maintain a calendar in his cubby. For each of the four days that the students are covering primary colors in class, students get to place a colored dot on their calendars: blue, yellow, or red. When the four days of the school week have passed (Monday–Thursday), what might the young girl's calendar look like?

One outcome would be four blue dots if the student chose blue each day. But consider that the first day (Monday) could be blue, and the next day (Tuesday) could be yellow, and Wednesday could be blue, and Thursday could be red. Or maybe Monday and Tuesday could be yellow, Wednesday could be blue, and Thursday could be red. Or maybe Monday, Tuesday, and Wednesday could be blue, and Thursday could be red, and so on and so forth.

As hard to follow as this seems now, we have only mentioned 3 of the 81 possible outcomes in terms of the four days of colors! Listing the other 78 outcomes would take several pages! Rather than listing outcomes in the manner described above (particularly when the situation has multiple stages, such as the multiple days in the case above), we often use a *tree diagram* to display all possible outcomes visually. Additionally, when the outcomes of each stage are the result of a chance experiment, tree diagrams are helpful for computing probabilities.

Example 1: Two Nights of Games

Imagine that a family decides to play a game each night. They all agree to use a tetrahedral die (i.e., a four-sided pyramidal die where each of four possible outcomes is equally likely—see the image at the end of this lesson) each night to randomly determine if they will play a board game (B) or a card game (C). The tree diagram mapping the possible overall outcomes over two consecutive nights will be developed below.

To make a tree diagram, first present all possibilities for the first stage (in this case, Monday).

Monday   **Tuesday**   **Outcome**

B

C

Then, from *each* branch of the first stage, attach all possibilities for the second stage (Tuesday).

| | Monday | Tuesday | Outcome |

Note: If the situation has more than two stages, this process would be repeated until all stages have been presented.

a. If BB represents two straight nights of board games, what does CB represent?

b. List the outcomes where exactly one board game is played over two days. How many outcomes were there?

Lesson 6:   Using Tree Diagrams to Represent a Sample
                              Space and to Calculate Probabilities

EUREKA
MATH

Example 2: Two Nights of Games (with Probabilities)

In Example 1, each night's outcome is the result of a chance experiment (rolling the tetrahedral die). Thus, there is a probability associated with each night's outcome.

By multiplying the probabilities of the outcomes from each stage, we can obtain the probability for each "branch of the tree." In this case, we can figure out the probability of each of our four outcomes: BB, BC, CB, and CC.

For this family, a card game will be played if the die lands showing a value of 1, and a board game will be played if the die lands showing a value of 2, 3, or 4. This makes the probability of a board game (B) on a given night 0.75.

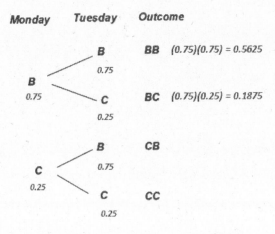

a.   The probabilities for two of the four outcomes are shown. Now, compute the probabilities for the two remaining outcomes.

b.   What is the probability that there will be exactly one night of board games over the two nights?

Exercises 1–3: Two Children

Two friends meet at a grocery store and remark that a neighboring family just welcomed their second child. It turns out that both children in this family are girls, and they are not twins. One of the friends is curious about what the chances are of having 2 girls in a family's first 2 births. Suppose that for each birth, the probability of a boy birth is 0.5 and the probability of a girl birth is also 0.5.

1. Draw a tree diagram demonstrating the four possible birth outcomes for a family with 2 children (no twins). Use the symbol B for the outcome of *boy* and G for the outcome of *girl*. Consider the first birth to be the first stage. (Refer to Example 1 if you need help getting started.)

2. Write in the probabilities of each stage's outcome to the tree diagram you developed above, and determine the probabilities for each of the 4 possible birth outcomes for a family with 2 children (no twins).

3. What is the probability of a family having 2 girls in this situation? Is that greater than or less than the probability of having exactly 1 girl in 2 births?

Lesson 6:   Using Tree Diagrams to Represent a Sample
            Space and to Calculate Probabilities

© 2019 Great Minds®. eureka-math.org

EUREKA
MATH®

Lesson Summary

Tree diagrams can be used to organize outcomes in the sample space for chance experiments that can be thought of as being performed in multiple stages. Tree diagrams are also useful for computing probabilities of events with more than one outcome.

Name _____   Date _____

In a laboratory experiment, two mice will be placed in a simple maze with one decision point where a mouse can turn either left (L) or right (R). When the first mouse arrives at the decision point, the direction it chooses is recorded. Then, the process is repeated for the second mouse.

1. Draw a tree diagram where the first stage represents the decision made by the first mouse and the second stage represents the decision made by the second mouse. Determine all four possible decision outcomes for the two mice.

2. If the probability of turning left is 0.5 and the probability of turning right is 0.5 for each mouse, what is the probability that only one of the two mice will turn left?

3. If the researchers add food in the simple maze such that the probability of each mouse turning left is now 0.7, what is the probability that only one of the two mice will turn left?

Lesson 6:   Using Tree Diagrams to Represent a Sample
             Space and to Calculate Probabilities

EUREKA
MATH

1. The Johnson family has decided to get two new pets, one for their son and one for their daughter. Mr. and Mrs. Johnson are allowing the kids to choose between a cat, a dog, or a bird. Each type of pet has an equally likely chance of being chosen.

    a. Using C for cat, D for dog, and B for bird, develop a tree diagram that shows the nine possible outcomes for the two different types of pets.

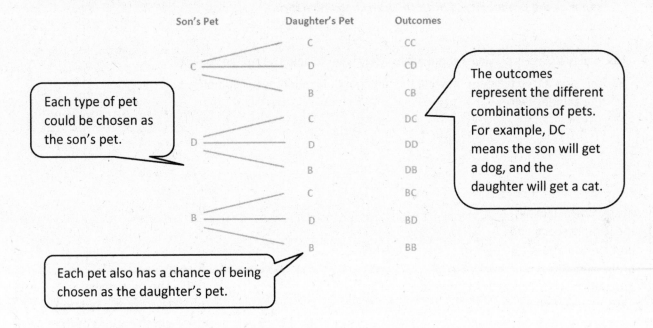

Each type of pet could be chosen as the son's pet.

Each pet also has a chance of being chosen as the daughter's pet.

The outcomes represent the different combinations of pets. For example, DC means the son will get a dog, and the daughter will get a cat.

    b. What is the probability of the son choosing a bird and the daughter choosing a cat?

$$\frac{1}{3} \cdot \frac{1}{3} = \frac{1}{9}$$

Since each pet has an equal chance to be chosen, the probability for each type of pet is $\frac{1}{3}$.

c. Is the probability that both children will choose a dog the same as the probability that both children will choose a bird? Explain.

The probability of both children choosing a dog is $\frac{1}{3} \cdot \frac{1}{3} = \frac{1}{9}$. The probability of both children choosing a bird is also $\frac{1}{3} \cdot \frac{1}{3} = \frac{1}{9}$. Therefore, the probability of both children choosing a dog is the same as the probability of both children choosing a bird.

2. Ms. Bailey's class is playing a game where they have to spin the spinner below.

a. Develop a tree diagram showing the nine possible outcomes of spinning the spinner twice.

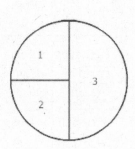

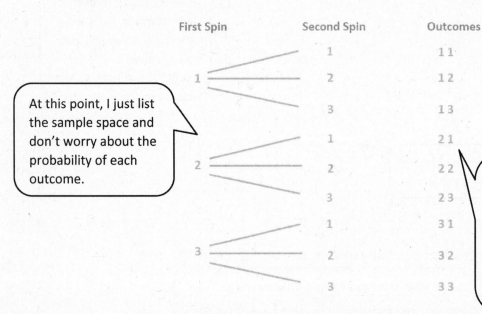

At this point, I just list the sample space and don't worry about the probability of each outcome.

The outcomes represent the different combinations of the two spins but does not yet indicate the probability of each outcome.

b. What is the probability that a student will spin a 2 on the first spin and a 3 on the second spin?

$(0.25)(0.5) = 0.125$

The probability of spinning a 2 is 0.25 because this section covers 25% of the spinner's area. The probability of spinning a 3 is 0.5 because this section covers 50% of the spinner's area.

c. What is the probability that the spinner will land on the 1 for both spins?

$(0.25)(0.25) = 0.0625$

The probability of spinning a 1 on either spin is 0.25 because this section covers 25% of the spinner's area.

Lesson 6:   Using Tree Diagrams to Represent a Sample Space and to Calculate Probabilities

EUREKA MATH

1. Imagine that a family of three (Alice, Bill, and Chester) plays bingo at home every night. Each night, the chance that any one of the three players will win is $\frac{1}{3}$.

   a. Using A for Alice wins, B for Bill wins, and C for Chester wins, develop a tree diagram that shows the nine possible outcomes for two consecutive nights of play.

   b. Is the probability that "Bill wins both nights" the same as the probability that "Alice wins the first night and Chester wins the second night"? Explain.

2. According to the Washington, D.C. Lottery's website for its Cherry Blossom Doubler instant scratch game, the chance of winning a prize on a given ticket is about 17%. Imagine that a person stops at a convenience store on the way home from work every Monday and Tuesday to buy a scratcher ticket to play the game.
   (Source: DC Lottery)

   a. Develop a tree diagram showing the four possible outcomes of playing over these two days. Call stage 1 "Monday," and use the symbols W for a winning ticket and L for a non-winning ticket.

   b. What is the chance that the player will not win on Monday but will win on Tuesday?

   c. What is the chance that the player will win at least once during the two-day period?

Image of Tetrahedral Die

Source: http://commons.wikimedia.org/wiki/File:4-sided_dice_250.jpg

Photo by Fantasy, via Wikimedia Commons, is licensed under CC BY-SA 3.0, http://creativecommons.org/licenses/by-sa/3.0/deed.en.

A previous lesson introduced *tree diagrams* as an effective method of displaying the possible outcomes of certain multistage chance experiments. Additionally, in such situations, tree diagrams were shown to be helpful for computing probabilities.

In those previous examples, diagrams primarily focused on cases with two stages. However, the basic principles of tree diagrams can apply to situations with more than two stages.

Example 1: Three Nights of Games

Recall a previous example where a family decides to play a game each night, and they all agree to use a tetrahedral die (a four-sided die in the shape of a pyramid where each of four possible outcomes is equally likely) each night to randomly determine if the game will be a board (B) or a card (C) game. The tree diagram mapping the possible overall outcomes over two consecutive nights was as follows:

Monday	Tuesday	Outcome
	B	BB
B		
	C	BC
	B	CB
C		
	C	CC

But how would the diagram change if you were interested in mapping the possible overall outcomes over three consecutive nights? To accommodate this additional third stage, you would take steps similar to what you did before. You would attach all possibilities for the third stage (Wednesday) to each branch of the previous stage (Tuesday).

Monday	Tuesday	Wednesday	Outcome
		B	BBB
	B		
B		C	BBC
		B	BCB
	C		
		C	BCC
		B	CBB
	B		
C		C	CBC
		B	CCB
	C		
		C	CCC

Exercises 1–3

1. If BBB represents three straight nights of board games, what does CBB represent?

2. List all outcomes where exactly two board games were played over three days. How many outcomes were there?

3. There are eight possible outcomes representing the three nights. Are the eight outcomes representing the three nights equally likely? Why or why not?

Example 2: Three Nights of Games (with Probabilities)

In Example 1, each night's outcome is the result of a chance experiment (rolling the four-sided die). Thus, there is a probability associated with each night's outcome.

By multiplying the probabilities of the outcomes from each stage, you can obtain the probability for each "branch of the tree." In this case, you can figure out the probability of each of our eight outcomes.

For this family, a card game will be played if the die lands showing a value of 1, and a board game will be played if the die lands showing a value of 2, 3, or 4. This makes the probability of a board game (B) on a given night 0.75.

Let's use a tree to examine the probabilities of the outcomes for the three days.

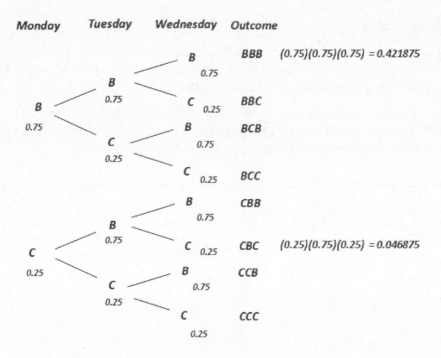

Exercises 4–6

4. Probabilities for two of the eight outcomes are shown. Calculate the approximate probabilities for the remaining six outcomes.

5. What is the probability that there will be exactly two nights of board games over the three nights?

6. What is the probability that the family will play at least one night of card games?

Exercises 7–10: Three Children

A neighboring family just welcomed their third child. It turns out that all 3 of the children in this family are girls, and they are not twins or triplets. Suppose that for each birth, the probability of a boy birth is 0.5, and the probability of a girl birth is also 0.5. What are the chances of having 3 girls in a family's first 3 births?

7. Draw a tree diagram showing the eight possible birth outcomes for a family with 3 children (no twins or triplets). Use the symbol B for the outcome of *boy* and G for the outcome of *girl*. Consider the first birth to be the first stage. (Refer to Example 1 if you need help getting started.)

8. Write in the probabilities of each stage's outcomes in the tree diagram you developed above, and determine the probabilities for each of the eight possible birth outcomes for a family with 3 children (no twins or triplets).

Lesson 7:   Calculating Probabilities of Compound Events

9. What is the probability of a family having 3 girls in this situation? Is that greater than or less than the probability of having exactly 2 girls in 3 births?

10. What is the probability of a family of 3 children having at least 1 girl?

Lesson Summary

The use of tree diagrams is not limited to cases of just two stages. For more complicated experiments, tree diagrams are used to organize outcomes and to assign probabilities. The tree diagram is a visual representation of outcomes that involve more than one event.

Name _____   Date _____

In a laboratory experiment, three mice will be placed in a simple maze that has just one decision point where a mouse can turn either left (L) or right (R). When the first mouse arrives at the decision point, the direction he chooses is recorded. The same is done for the second and the third mouse.

1. Draw a tree diagram where the first stage represents the decision made by the first mouse, the second stage represents the decision made by the second mouse, and so on. Determine all eight possible outcomes of the decisions for the three mice.

2. Use the tree diagram from Problem 1 to help answer the following question. If, for each mouse, the probability of turning left is 0.5 and the probability of turning right is 0.5, what is the probability that only one of the three mice will turn left?

3. If the researchers conducting the experiment add food in the simple maze such that the probability of each mouse turning left is now 0.7, what is the probability that only one of the three mice will turn left? To answer the question, use the tree diagram from Problem 1.

EUREKA
MATH

Kaia's four kids are arguing over the type of game they want to play. Therefore, Kaia agrees to roll a four-sided die with sides numbered 1, 2, 3, and 4. If the die lands on a 1, 2, or 3, they will play a matching game, and if the die lands on a 4, they will play a card game.

a. Kaia agrees to play three games with her kids. Create a tree diagram to show the different types of games they may play.

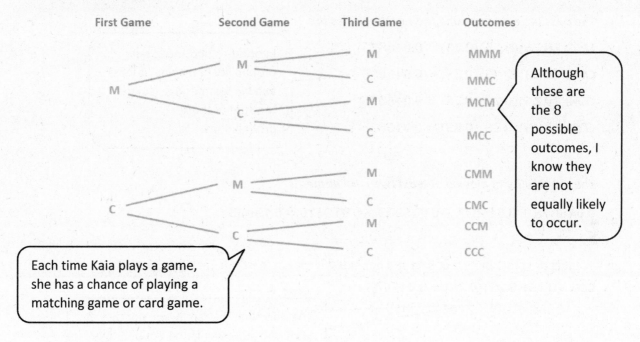

Each time Kaia plays a game, she has a chance of playing a matching game or card game.

Although these are the 8 possible outcomes, I know they are not equally likely to occur.

b. What is the probability that all three games will be a matching game?

MMM: $(0.75)(0.75)(0.75) = 0.421875$

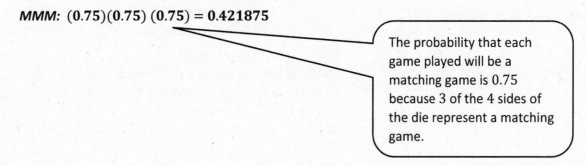

The probability that each game played will be a matching game is 0.75 because 3 of the 4 sides of the die represent a matching game.

c. What is the probability that at least two card games will be played?

   The possible outcomes and their probabilities are

   MCC: $(0.75)(0.25)(0.25) = 0.046875$

   CMC: $(0.25)(0.75)(0.25) = 0.046875$

   CCM: $(0.25)(0.25)(0.75) = 0.046875$

   CCC: $(0.25)(0.25)(0.25) = 0.015625$

> The probability that a card game will be played is 0.25 because 1 of the 4 sides of the die represents a card game.

> In order to find the total probability of playing at least two card games, I calculate the sum of these probabilities.

   The probability of playing at least two card games is

   $0.046875 + 0.046875 + 0.046875 + 0.015625 = 0.15625$

d. What is the probability that Kaia and her kids will play at least one matching game?

   CCC: $(0.25)(0.25)(0.25) = 0.015625$

> The only time the family will not play at least one matching game is when they play three card games.

   The probability of playing at least one matching game is

   $1 - 0.015625 = 0.984375$

> The probability of playing at least one matching game is the total probability (which is 1) minus the probability of playing three card games.

EUREKA
MATH

1. According to the Washington, D.C. Lottery's website for its Cherry Blossom Double instant scratch game, the chance of winning a prize on a given ticket is about 17%. Imagine that a person stops at a convenience store on the way home from work every Monday, Tuesday, and Wednesday to buy a scratcher ticket and plays the game.
   (Source: DC Lottery)

   a. Develop a tree diagram showing the eight possible outcomes of playing over these three days. Call stage one "Monday," and use the symbols W for a winning ticket and L for a non-winning ticket.

   b. What is the probability that the player will not win on Monday but will win on Tuesday and Wednesday?

   c. What is the probability that the player will win at least once during the 3-day period?

2. A survey company is interested in conducting a statewide poll prior to an upcoming election. They are only interested in talking to registered voters.

   Imagine that 55% of the registered voters in the state are male and 45% are female. Also, consider that the distribution of ages may be different for each group. In this state, 30% of male registered voters are age 18–24, 37% are age 25–64, and 33% are 65 or older. 32% of female registered voters are age 18–24, 26% are age 25–64, and 42% are 65 or older.

   The following tree diagram describes the distribution of registered voters. The probability of selecting a male registered voter age 18–24 is 0.165.

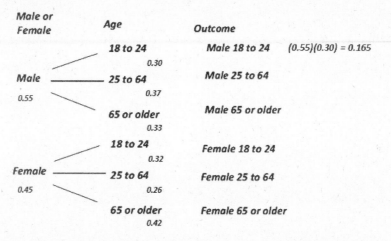

   a. What is the chance that the polling company will select a registered female voter age 65 or older?

   b. What is the chance that the polling company will select any registered voter age 18–24?

Have you ever watched the beginning of a professional football game? After the traditional handshakes, a coin is tossed to determine which team gets to kick off first. The toss of a fair coin is often used to make decisions between two groups.

Example 1: Why a Coin?

Coins were discussed in previous lessons of this module. What is special about a coin? In most cases, a coin has two different sides: a head side (heads) and a tail side (tails). The sample space for tossing a coin is {heads, tails}. If each outcome has an equal chance of occurring when the coin is tossed, then the probability of getting heads is $\frac{1}{2}$, or 0.5. The probability of getting tails is also 0.5. Note that the sum of these probabilities is 1.

The probabilities formed using the sample space and what we know about coins are called the *theoretical* probabilities. Using observed relative frequencies is another method to estimate the probabilities of heads or tails. A relative frequency is the proportion derived from the number of the observed outcomes of an event divided by the total number of outcomes. Recall from earlier lessons that a relative frequency can be expressed as a fraction, a decimal, or a percent. Is the estimate of a probability from this method close to the theoretical probability? The following example investigates how relative frequencies can be used to estimate probabilities.

Beth tosses a coin 10 times and records her results. Here are the results from the 10 tosses:

Toss	1	2	3	4	5	6	7	8	9	10
Result	H	H	T	H	H	H	T	T	T	H

The total number of heads divided by the total number of tosses is the relative frequency of heads. It is the proportion of the time that heads occurred on these tosses. The total number of tails divided by the total number of tosses is the relative frequency of tails.

a. Beth started to complete the following table as a way to investigate the relative frequencies. For each outcome, the total number of tosses increased. The total number of heads or tails observed so far depends on the outcome of the current toss. Complete this table for the 10 tosses recorded in the previous table.

Toss	Outcome	Total Number of Heads So Far	Relative Frequency of Heads So Far (to the nearest hundredth)	Total Number of Tails So Far	Relative Frequency of Tails So Far (to the nearest hundredth)
1	H	1	$\frac{1}{1} = 1$	0	$\frac{0}{1} = 0$
2	H	2	$\frac{2}{2} = 1$	0	$\frac{0}{2} = 0$
3	T	2	$\frac{2}{3} \approx 0.67$	1	$\frac{1}{3} \approx 0.33$
4					
5					
6					
7					
8					
9					
10					

b. What is the sum of the relative frequency of heads and the relative frequency of tails for each row of the table?

Lesson 8:   The Difference Between Theoretical Probabilities
             and Estimated Probabilities

EUREKA
MATH

c. Beth's results can also be displayed using a graph. Use the values of the relative frequency of heads so far from the table in part (a) to complete the graph below.

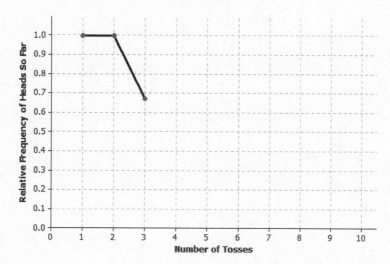

d. Beth continued tossing the coin and recording the results for a total of 40 tosses. Here are the results of the next 30 tosses:

Toss	11	12	13	14	15	16	17	18	19	20
Result	T	H	T	H	T	H	H	T	H	T

Toss	21	22	23	24	25	26	27	28	29	30
Result	H	T	T	H	T	T	T	T	H	T

Toss	31	32	33	34	35	36	37	38	39	40
Result	H	T	H	T	H	T	H	H	T	T

As the number of tosses increases, the relative frequency of heads changes. Complete the following table for the 40 coin tosses:

Number of Tosses	Total Number of Heads So Far	Relative Frequency of Heads So Far (to the nearest hundredth)
1		
5		
10		
15		
20		
25		
30		
35		
40		

e. Use the relative frequency of heads so far from the table in part (d) to complete the graph below for the total number of tosses of 1, 5, 10, 15, 20, 25, 30, 35, and 40.

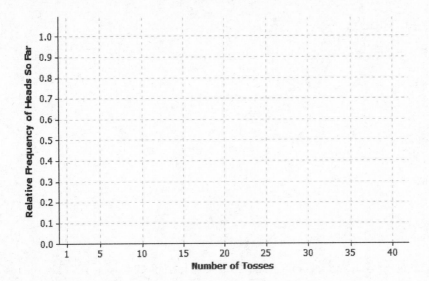

f. What do you notice about the changes in the relative frequency of the number of heads so far as the number of tosses increases?

g. If you tossed the coin 100 times, what do you think the relative frequency of heads would be? Explain your answer.

h. Based on the graph and the relative frequencies, what would you estimate the probability of getting heads to be? Explain your answer.

Lesson 8:   The Difference Between Theoretical Probabilities
                             and Estimated Probabilities

EUREKA
MATH

i. How close is your estimate in part (h) to the theoretical probability of 0.5? Would the estimate of this probability have been as good if Beth had only tossed the coin a few times instead of 40?

The value you gave in part (h) is an estimate of the theoretical probability and is called an *experimental* or *estimated probability*.

Exercises 1–8

Beth received nine more pennies. She securely taped them together to form a small stack. The top penny of her stack showed heads, and the bottom penny showed tails. If Beth tosses the stack, what outcomes could she observe?

1. Beth wanted to determine the probability of getting heads when she tosses the stack. Do you think this probability is the same as the probability of getting heads with just one coin? Explain your answer.

2. Make a sturdy stack of 10 pennies in which one end of the stack has a penny showing heads and the other end tails. Make sure the pennies are taped securely, or you may have a mess when you toss the stack. Toss the stack to observe possible outcomes. What is the sample space for tossing a stack of 10 pennies taped together? Do you think the probability of each outcome of the sample space is equal? Explain your answer.

3. Record the results of 10 tosses. Complete the following table of the relative frequencies of heads for your 10 tosses:

Toss	1	2	3	4	5	6	7	8	9	10
Result										
Relative Frequency of Heads So Far										

4. Based on the value of the relative frequencies of heads so far, what would you estimate the probability of getting heads to be?

5. Toss the stack of 10 pennies another 20 times. Complete the following table:

Toss	11	12	13	14	15	16	17	18	19	20
Result										

Toss	21	22	23	24	25	26	27	28	29	30
Result										

6. Summarize the relative frequency of heads so far by completing the following table:

Number of Tosses	Total Number of Heads So Far	Relative Frequency of Heads So Far (to the nearest hundredth)
1		
5		
10		
15		
20		
25		
30		

Lesson 8:   The Difference Between Theoretical Probabilities and Estimated Probabilities

EUREKA MATH®

7. Based on the relative frequencies for the 30 tosses, what is your estimate of the probability of getting heads? Can you compare this estimate to a theoretical probability like you did in the first example? Explain your answer.

8. Create another stack of pennies. Consider creating a stack using 5 pennies, 15 pennies, or 20 pennies taped together in the same way you taped the pennies to form a stack of 10 pennies. Again, make sure the pennies are taped securely, or you might have a mess!

   Toss the stack you made 30 times. Record the outcome for each toss:

Toss	1	2	3	4	5	6	7	8	9	10
Result										

Toss	11	12	13	14	15	16	17	18	19	20
Result										

Toss	21	22	23	24	25	26	27	28	29	30
Result										

Lesson Summary

- Observing the long-run relative frequency of an event from a chance experiment (or the proportion of an event derived from a long sequence of observations) approximates the theoretical probability of the event.

- After a long sequence of observations, the observed relative frequencies get close to the probability of the event occurring.

- When it is not possible to compute the theoretical probabilities of chance experiments, then the long-run relative frequencies (or the proportion of events derived from a long sequence of observations) can be used as estimated probabilities of events.

Lesson 8:   The Difference Between Theoretical Probabilities
and Estimated Probabilities

EUREKA
MATH

Name _____   Date _____

1. Which of the following graphs would *not* represent the relative frequencies of heads when tossing 1 penny? Explain your answer.

Graph A   Graph B

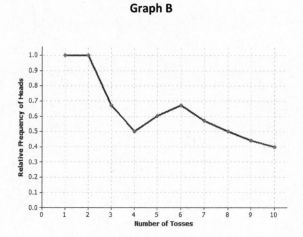

2. Jerry indicated that after tossing a penny 30 times, the relative frequency of heads was 0.47 (to the nearest hundredth). He indicated that after 31 times, the relative frequency of heads was 0.55. Are Jerry's summaries correct? Why or why not?

3. Jerry observed 5 heads in 100 tosses of his coin. Do you think this was a fair coin? Why or why not?

Predicting Theoretical Probability

1. Consider the data you collected in class when you taped 10 pennies in a tall stack. Would the probability of landing on a head be more likely or less likely if we taped more than 10 pennies in a stack? Explain.

   As we create a bigger stack, the probability of landing on a head becomes less likely because the larger stacks will land on their sides more often.

   > I can perform the experiment if I am not sure how to answer this question.

   > Large stacks of pennies are difficult to balance standing upright, so they will not land standing upright very often.

2. If you created a stack of pennies shorter than 10 pennies, how would the probability of landing on a head change?

   A smaller stack of pennies would increase the probablity of landing on a head because it is easier to stand small stacks upright.

   > As the stack of pennies gets smaller, the probability of landing on a head increases.

Estimated Probability

3. Assume we taped 3 pennies into a stack, tossed the stack 20 times, and recorded our results in the table below.

Number of Tosses	Total Number of Heads so Far	Relative Frequency of Heads so Far (to the nearest hundredth)
1	0	$\dfrac{0}{1} = 0.0$
5	2	$\dfrac{2}{5} = 0.4$
10	3	$\dfrac{3}{10} = 0.3$
15	5	$\dfrac{5}{15} = 0.\overline{3}$
20	6	$\dfrac{6}{20} = 0.3$

> In order to calculate the relative frequency, I set up a fraction to show the number of heads out of the total number of tosses.

a. Complete the table by calculating the relative frequencies. If necessary, round to the nearest hundredth.

b. What is your estimated probability that our stack of pennies will land heads up when tossed? Explain.

   My estimated probability that our stack of pennies will land heads up is 0.3 *because most of the relative frequencies are close to this number.*

> Answers will vary but should be based on the relative frequencies.

EUREKA MATH

1. If you created a stack of 15 pennies taped together, do you think the probability of getting a heads on a toss of the stack would be different than for a stack of 10 pennies? Explain your answer.

2. If you created a stack of 20 pennies taped together, what do you think the probability of getting a heads on a toss of the stack would be? Explain your answer.

3. Based on your work in this lesson, complete the following table of the relative frequencies of heads for the stack you created:

Number of Tosses	Total Number of Heads So Far	Relative Frequency of Heads So Far (to the nearest hundredth)
1		
5		
10		
15		
20		
25		
30		

4. What is your estimate of the probability that your stack of pennies will land heads up when tossed? Explain your answer.

5. Is there a theoretical probability you could use to compare to the estimated probability? Explain your answer.

Exploratory Challenge: Game Show—Picking Blue!

Imagine, for a moment, the following situation: You and your classmates are contestants on a quiz show called *Picking Blue!* There are two bags in front of you, Bag A and Bag B. Each bag contains red and blue chips. You are told that one of the bags has exactly the same number of blue chips as red chips. But you are told nothing about the ratio of blue to red chips in the other bag.

Each student in your class will be asked to select either Bag A or Bag B. Starting with Bag A, a chip is randomly selected from the bag. If a blue chip is drawn, all of the students in your class who selected Bag A win a blue token. The chip is put back in the bag. After mixing up the chips in the bag, another chip is randomly selected from the bag. If the chip is blue, the students who picked Bag A win another blue token. After the chip is placed back into the bag, the process continues until a red chip is picked. When a red chip is picked, the game moves to Bag B. A chip from the Bag B is then randomly selected. If it is blue, all of the students who selected Bag B win a blue token. But if the chip is red, the game is over. Just like for Bag A, if the chip is blue, the process repeats until a red chip is picked from the bag. When the game is over, the students with the greatest number of blue tokens are considered the winning team.

Without any information about the bags, you would probably select a bag simply by guessing. But surprisingly, the show's producers are going to allow you to do some research before you select a bag. For the next 20 minutes, you can pull a chip from either one of the two bags, look at the chip, and then put the chip back in the bag. You can repeat this process as many times as you want within the 20 minutes. At the end of 20 minutes, you must make your final decision and select which of the bags you want to use in the game.

Getting Started

Assume that the producers of the show do not want to give away a lot of their blue tokens. As a result, if one bag has the same number of red and blue chips, do you think the other bag would have more or fewer blue chips than red chips? Explain your answer.

Planning the Research

Your teacher will provide you with two bags labeled A and B. You have 20 minutes to experiment with pulling chips one at a time from the bags. After you examine a chip, you must put it back in the bag. Remember, no peeking in the bags, as that will disqualify you from the game. You can pick chips from just one bag, or you can pick chips from one bag and then the other bag.

Use the results from 20 minutes of research to determine which bag you will choose for the game.

Provide a description outlining how you will carry out your research.

Carrying Out the Research

Share your plan with your teacher. Your teacher will verify whether your plan is within the rules of the quiz show. Approving your plan does not mean, however, that your teacher is indicating that your research method offers the most accurate way to determine which bag to select. If your teacher approves your research, carry out your plan as outlined. Record the results from your research, as directed by your teacher.

Playing the Game

After the research has been conducted, the competition begins. First, your teacher will shake up Bag A. A chip is selected. If the chip is blue, all students who selected Bag A win an imaginary blue token. The chip is put back in the bag, and the process continues. When a red chip is picked from Bag A, students selecting Bag A have completed the competition. Your teacher will now shake up Bag B. A chip is selected. If it is blue, all students who selected Bag B win an imaginary blue token. The process continues until a red chip is picked. At that point, the game is over.

How many blue tokens did you win?

Lesson 9: Comparing Estimated Probabilities to
Probabilities Predicted by a Model

Examining Your Results

At the end of the game, your teacher will open the bags and reveal how many blue and red chips were in each bag. Answer the questions that follow. After you have answered these questions, discuss them with your class.

1. Before you played the game, what were you trying to learn about the bags from your research?

2. What did you expect to happen when you pulled chips from the bag with the same number of blue and red chips? Did the bag that you thought had the same number of blue and red chips yield the results you expected?

3. How confident were you in predicting which bag had the same number of blue and red chips? Explain.

4. What bag did you select to use in the competition, and why?

5. If you were the show's producers, how would you make up the second bag? (Remember, one bag has the same number of red and blue chips.)

6. If you picked a chip from Bag B 100 times and found that you picked each color exactly 50 times, would you know for sure that Bag B was the one with equal numbers of each color?

Lesson Summary

- The long-run relative frequencies can be used as estimated probabilities of events.

- Collecting data on a game or chance experiment is one way to estimate the probability of an outcome.

- The more data collected on the outcomes from a game or chance experiment, the closer the estimates of the probabilities are likely to be the actual probabilities.

Picking Green! This is a game similar to the one you played in class, where you try to pick as many green chips as possible before picking one white chip. One bag has the same number of green and white chips, and the ratio of green to white chips in the second bag is unknown.

After experimenting, I either choose Bag A or Bag B in hopes of picking the most green chips while avoiding white chips.

Laura and Carly completed an experiment, and their results are shown in the tables below.

Laura's Results:

Bag	Number of Green Chips Picked	Number of White Chips Picked
A	35	15
B	22	28

Carly's Results:

Bag	Number of Green Chips Picked	Number of White Chips Picked
A	7	8
B	9	6

1. If all you know about the bags are the results from Laura's research, which bag would you select for the game? Explain.

   I would choose Bag A because Laura's results show that she picked a lot more green chips than white chips from Bag A.

   In order to win, I want to pick the bag that I think has the most green chips.

2. If all you know about the bags are the results from Carly's research, which bag would you select for the game? Explain.

   I would choose Bag B because Carly's results show that she picked a few more green chips than white chips from Bag B.

   Both Bag A and Bag B had similar results, but Carly picked a few more green chips from Bag B.

3. Whose research gives you a better indication of the makeup of green and white chips in each bag? Explain.

   Laura's results would be a better indication of the makeup of green and white chips in each bag because she collected more data than Carly.

   The more data we collect, the closer the outcome is to the theoretical probability.

   > I know that the more outcomes carried out, the closer the relative frequency is to the theoretical probability.

4. If there were three colors of chips in each bag, how would you collect data in order to choose a bag?

   My data collection would be the same. I would just have to extend my table to include a third color.

Lesson 9:   Comparing Estimated Probabilities to
             Probabilities Predicted by a Model

EUREKA
MATH®

Jerry and Michael played a game similar to *Picking Blue!* The following results are from their research using the same two bags:

Jerry's research:

	Number of Red Chips Picked	Number of Blue Chips Picked
Bag A	2	8
Bag B	3	7

Michael's research:

	Number of Red Chips Picked	Number of Blue Chips Picked
Bag A	28	12
Bag B	22	18

1. If all you knew about the bags were the results of Jerry's research, which bag would you select for the game? Explain your answer.

2. If all you knew about the bags were the results of Michael's research, which bag would you select for the game? Explain your answer.

3. Does Jerry's research or Michael's research give you a better indication of the makeup of the blue and red chips in each bag? Explain why you selected this research.

4. Assume there are 12 chips in each bag. Use either Jerry's or Michael's research to estimate the number of red and blue chips in each bag. Then, explain how you made your estimates.

    Bag A

    Number of red chips:

    Number of blue chips:

    Bag B

    Number of red chips:

    Number of blue chips:

5. In a different game of *Picking Blue!*, two bags each contain red, blue, green, and yellow chips. One bag contains the same number of red, blue, green, and yellow chips. In the second bag, half of the chips are blue. Describe a plan for determining which bag has more blue chips than any of the other colors.

In previous lessons, you estimated probabilities of events by collecting data empirically or by establishing a theoretical probability model. There are real problems for which those methods may be difficult or not practical to use. Simulation is a procedure that will allow you to answer questions about real problems by running experiments that closely resemble the real situation.

It is often important to know the probabilities of real-life events that may not have known theoretical probabilities. Scientists, engineers, and mathematicians design simulations to answer questions that involve topics such as diseases, water flow, climate changes, or functions of an engine. Results from the simulations are used to estimate probabilities that help researchers understand problems and provide possible solutions to these problems.

Example 1: Families

How likely is it that a family with three children has all boys or all girls?

Let's assume that a child is equally likely to be a boy or a girl. Instead of observing the result of actual births, a toss of a fair coin could be used to simulate a birth. If the toss results in heads (H), then we could say a boy was born; if the toss results in tails (T), then we could say a girl was born. If the coin is fair (i.e., heads and tails are equally likely), then getting a boy or a girl is equally likely.

Exercises 1–2

Suppose that a family has three children. To simulate the genders of the three children, the coin or number cube or a card would need to be used three times, once for each child. For example, three tosses of the coin resulted in HHT, representing a family with two boys and one girl. Note that HTH and THH also represent two boys and one girl.

1. Suppose that when a prime number (P) is rolled on the number cube, it simulates a boy birth, and a non-prime (N) simulates a girl birth. Using such a number cube, list the outcomes that would simulate a boy birth and those that simulate a girl birth. Are the boy and girl birth outcomes equally likely?

2. Suppose that one card is drawn from a regular deck of cards. A red card (R) simulates a boy birth, and a black card (B) simulates a girl birth. Describe how a family of three children could be simulated.

Example 2

Simulation provides an estimate for the probability that a family of three children would have three boys or three girls by performing three tosses of a fair coin many times. Each sequence of three tosses is called a *trial*. If a trial results in either HHH or TTT, then the trial represents all boys or all girls, which is the event that we are interested in. These trials would be called a *success*. If a trial results in any other order of H's and T's, then it is called a *failure*.

The estimate for the probability that a family has either three boys or three girls based on the simulation is the number of successes divided by the number of trials. Suppose 100 trials are performed, and that in those 100 trials, 28 resulted in either HHH or TTT. Then, the estimated probability that a family of three children has either three boys or three girls would be $\frac{28}{100}$, or 0.28.

Exercises 3–5

3. Find an estimate of the probability that a family with three children will have exactly one girl using the following outcomes of 50 trials of tossing a fair coin three times per trial. Use H to represent a boy birth and T to represent a girl birth.

HHT   HTH   HHH   TTH   THT   THT   HTT   HHH   TTH   HHH

HHT   TTT   HHT   TTH   HHH   HTH   THH   TTT   THT   THT

THT   HHH   THH   HTT   HTH   TTT   HTT   HHH   TTH   THT

THH   HHT   TTT   TTH   HTT   THH   HTT   HTH   TTT   HHH

HTH   HTH   THT   TTH   TTT   HHT   HHT   THT   TTT   HTT

EUREKA
MATH®

4. Perform a simulation of 50 trials by rolling a fair number cube in order to find an estimate of the probability that a family with three children will have exactly one girl.

   a. Specify what outcomes of one roll of a fair number cube will represent a boy and what outcomes will represent a girl.

   b. Simulate 50 trials, keeping in mind that one trial requires three rolls of the number cube. List the results of your 50 trials.

   c. Calculate the estimated probability.

5. Calculate the theoretical probability that a family with three children will have exactly one girl.

   a. List the possible outcomes for a family with three children. For example, one possible outcome is BBB (all three children are boys).

   b. Assume that having a boy and having a girl are equally likely. Calculate the theoretical probability that a family with three children will have exactly one girl.

c. Compare it to the estimated probabilities found in parts (a) and (b).

Example 3: Basketball Player

Suppose that, on average, a basketball player makes about three out of every four foul shots. In other words, she has a 75% chance of making each foul shot she takes. Since a coin toss produces equally likely outcomes, it could not be used in a simulation for this problem.

Instead, a number cube could be used by specifying that the numbers 1, 2, or 3 represent a hit, the number 4 represents a miss, and the numbers 5 and 6 would be ignored. Based on the following 50 trials of rolling a fair number cube, find an estimate of the probability that she makes five or six of the six foul shots she takes.

441323	342124	442123	422313	441243
124144	333434	243122	232323	224341
121411	321341	111422	114232	414411
344221	222442	343123	122111	322131
131224	213344	321241	311214	241131
143143	243224	323443	324243	214322
214411	423221	311423	142141	411312
343214	123131	242124	141132	343122
121142	321442	121423	443431	214433
331113	311313	211411	433434	323314

EUREKA MATH

Name _____   Date _____

1. Nathan is your school's star soccer player. When he takes a shot on goal, he typically scores half of the time. Suppose that he takes six shots in a game. To estimate the probability of the number of goals Nathan makes, use simulation with a number cube. One roll of a number cube represents one shot.

    a. Specify what outcome of a number cube you want to represent a goal scored by Nathan in one shot.

    b. For this problem, what represents a trial of taking six shots?

    c. Perform and list the results of ten trials of this simulation.

    d. Identify the number of goals Nathan made in each of the ten trials you did in part (c).

    e. Based on your ten trials, what is your estimate of the probability that Nathan scores three goals if he takes six shots in a game?

2. Suppose that Pat scores 40% of the shots he takes in a soccer game. If he takes six shots in a game, what would one simulated trial look like using a number cube in your simulation?

Predicting a Hamster's Path

1. Samantha bought her hamster a new maze for his cage, which is shown below. The hamster can only exit the maze at one point. At each point where the hamster has to decide which direction to go, assume that it is equally likely to go in either direction. At each decision point, A, B, and C, it must decide whether to go left (L) or right (R).

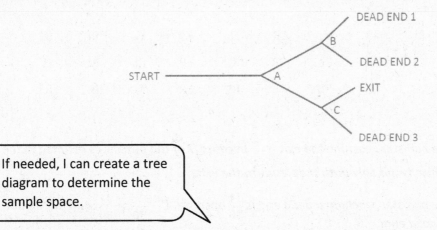

> If needed, I can create a tree diagram to determine the sample space.

a. List the possible paths of a sample space for the paths the hamster can take. For example, if the hamster goes left at decision point A and then right at decision point B, then the path would be denoted LR.

   The sample space is LL, LR, RL, RR.

b. Are the paths in the sample space equally likely? Explain.

   At each decision point there are two choices, which are equally likely. Therefore, each path in the sample space is as equally likely as the other paths.

c. What is the theoretical probability of the hamster finding the exit?

> The only path that leads to the exit is RL.

   Only one of the four possible paths will lead the hamster to the exit.

   Therefore, the probability of the hamster reaching the exit is $\frac{1}{4}$.

d. What is the theoretical probability of the hamster reaching a dead end?

Three of the four possible paths will lead to a dead end, which means the probability is $\frac{3}{4}$.

e. Based on the set of simulated paths, estimate the probabilities that the hamster arrives at the exit and any of the dead ends. Explain.

RR	RL	LR	LL	LR	LL	RR	LL	RR	RL
LL	LR	LR	RL	RR	RL	LR	RL	RL	LL
RL	LR	LL	RR	RL	RL	LR	RR	LL	RR

> There are 30 trials listed here.

The probability of the hamster reaching the exit is $\frac{9}{30}$ because 9 of the outcomes resulted in the hamster going RL, which is the only path that leads to the exit.

The probability of the hamster reaching a dead end is $\frac{21}{30}$ because $1 - \frac{9}{30} = \frac{21}{30}$, and all the other paths lead toward a dead end.

Using Simulation with a Dart Board

2. Suppose a dart board is made up of the 6 × 6 grid of squares shown below. Also, suppose that when a dart is thrown, it is equally likely to land on any one of the 36 squares. A point is won if the dart lands on one of the 12 red squares. Zero points are earned if the dart lands in a white square.

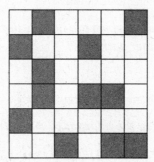

a. For one throw of a dart, what is the probability of winning a point?

$$\frac{12}{36} = \frac{1}{3}$$

> I win a point if I land on one of the 12 red squares. I also know there are 36 total squares.

Lesson 10:   Conducting a Simulation to Estimate the Probability of an Event

© 2019 Great Minds®. eureka-math.org

EUREKA MATH

b. Dylan wants to use a six-sided number cube with the sides numbered 1 through 6 to simulate the results of one dart. How could he assign the six numbers on the number cube to create an appropriate simulation?

> Since there are six different numbers on a number cube, I know that 2 of the numbers must represent winning a point because $\frac{2}{6}$ is equal to $\frac{1}{3}$. The other four numbers will represent not winning a point.

Dylan can assign 1 and 2 to simulate winning a point and the numbers 3, 4, 5, and 6 to simulate not winning a point.

Suppose a game consists of throwing four darts. A trial consists of four rolls of the number cube. Based on your suggestion in part (b) and the following simulated rolls,

1234	3321	5624	2451	6253
1625	3452	6115	2511	2361
5436	2251	5461	1253	6344
5513	6634	5112	3426	5534

c. What is the probability that none of the four darts will score a point?

Note: These four trials are circled above.

$$\frac{4}{20} = \frac{1}{5}$$

> I determine how many of the 20 trials do not include a 1 or 2 because these numbers represent winning a point.

d. What is the probability that three of the darts will score a point?

Note: These three trials are boxed above.

$$\frac{3}{20}$$

> I determine how many of the 20 trials have three rolls that are either a 1 or 2.

1. A mouse is placed at the start of the maze shown below. If it reaches station B, it is given a reward. At each point where the mouse has to decide which direction to go, assume that it is equally likely to go in either direction. At each decision point 1, 2, 3, it must decide whether to go left (L) or right (R). It cannot go backward.

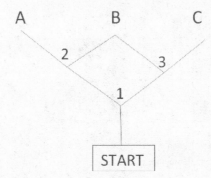

a. Create a theoretical model of probabilities for the mouse to arrive at terminal points A, B, and C.

    i. List the possible paths of a sample space for the paths the mouse can take. For example, if the mouse goes left at decision point 1 and then right at decision point 2, then the path would be denoted LR.

    ii. Are the paths in your sample space equally likely? Explain.

    iii. What are the theoretical probabilities that a mouse reaches terminal points A, B, and C? Explain.

b. Based on the following set of simulated paths, estimate the probabilities that the mouse arrives at points A, B, and C.

RR	RR	RL	LL	LR	RL	LR	LL	LR	RR
LR	RL	LR	RR	RL	LR	RR	LL	RL	RL
LL	LR	LR	LL	RR	RR	RL	LL	RR	LR
RR	LR	RR	LR	LR	LL	LR	RL	RL	LL

c. How do the simulated probabilities in part (b) compare to the theoretical probabilities of part (a)?

2. Suppose that a dartboard is made up of the 8 × 8 grid of squares shown below. Also, suppose that when a dart is thrown, it is equally likely to land on any one of the 64 squares. A point is won if the dart lands on one of the 16 black squares. Zero points are earned if the dart lands in a white square.

a. For one throw of a dart, what is the probability of winning a point? Note that a point is won if the dart lands on a black square.

b. Lin wants to use a number cube to simulate the result of one dart. She suggests that 1 on the number cube could represent a win. Getting 2, 3, or 4 could represent no point scored. She says that she would ignore getting a 5 or 6. Is Lin's suggestion for a simulation appropriate? Explain why you would use it, or if not, how you would change it.

c. Suppose a game consists of throwing a dart three times. A trial consists of three rolls of the number cube. Based on Lin's suggestion in part (b) and the following simulated rolls, estimate the probability of scoring two points in three darts.

324	332	411	322	124
224	221	241	111	223
321	332	112	433	412
443	322	424	412	433
144	322	421	414	111
242	244	222	331	224
113	223	333	414	212
431	233	314	212	241
421	222	222	112	113
212	413	341	442	324

d. The theoretical probability model for winning 0, 1, 2, and 3 points in three throws of the dart as described in this problem is:

i.   Winning 0 points has a probability of 0.42.

ii. Winning 1 point has a probability of 0.42.

iii. Winning 2 points has a probability of 0.14.

iv. Winning 3 points has a probability of 0.02.

Use the simulated rolls in part (c) to build a model of winning 0, 1, 2, and 3 points, and compare it to the theoretical model.

Lesson 10:   Conducting a Simulation to Estimate the Probability of an Event

Example 1: Simulation

In the last lesson, we used coins, number cubes, and cards to carry out simulations. Another option is putting identical pieces of paper or colored disks into a container, mixing them thoroughly, and then choosing one.

For example, if a basketball player typically makes five out of eight foul shots, then a colored disk could be used to simulate a foul shot. A green disk could represent a made shot, and a red disk could represent a miss. You could put five green and three red disks in a container, mix them, and then choose one to represent a foul shot. If the color of the disk is green, then the shot is made. If the color of the disk is red, then the shot is missed. This procedure simulates one foul shot.

a. Using colored disks, describe how one at bat could be simulated for a baseball player who has a batting average of 0.300. Note that a batting average of 0.300 means the player gets a hit (on average) three times out of every ten times at bat. Be sure to state clearly what a color represents.

b. Using colored disks, describe how one at bat could be simulated for a player who has a batting average of 0.273. Note that a batting average of 0.273 means that on average, the player gets 273 hits out of 1,000 at bats.

Example 2: Using Random Number Tables

Why is using colored disks not practical for the situation described in Example 1(b)? Another way to carry out a simulation is to use a random number table, or a random number generator. In a random number table, the digits 0, 1, 2, 3, 4, 5, 6, 7, 8, and 9 occur equally often in the long run. Pages and pages of random numbers can be found online.

For example, here are three lines of random numbers. The space after every five digits is only for ease of reading. Ignore the spaces when using the table.

25256 65205 72597 00562 12683 90674 78923 96568 32177 33855

76635 92290 88864 72794 14333 79019 05943 77510 74051 87238

07895 86481 94036 12749 24005 80718 13144 66934 54730 77140

To use the random number table to simulate an at bat for the 0.273 hitter in Example 1(b), you could use a three-digit number to represent one at bat. The three-digit numbers 000–272 could represent a hit, and the three-digit numbers 273–999 could represent a non-hit. Using the random numbers above and starting at the beginning of the first line, the first three-digit random number is 252, which is between 000 and 272, so that simulated at bat is a hit. The next three-digit random number is 566, which is a non-hit.

Continuing on the first line of the random numbers above, what would the hit/non-hit outcomes be for the next six at bats? Be sure to state the random number and whether it simulates a hit or non-hit.

Example 3: Baseball Player

A batter typically gets to bat four times in a ball game. Consider the 0.273 hitter from the previous example. Use the following steps (and the random numbers shown above) to estimate that player's probability of getting at least three hits (three or four) in four times at bat.

a. Describe what one trial is for this problem.

b. Describe when a trial is called a success and when it is called a failure.

c.   Simulate 12 trials. (Continue to work as a class, or let students work with a partner.)

d.   Use the results of the simulation to estimate the probability that a 0.273 hitter gets three or four hits in four times at bat. Compare your estimate with other groups.

Example 4: Birth Month

In a group of more than 12 people, is it likely that at least two people, maybe more, will have the same birth month? Why? Try it in your class.

Now, suppose that the same question is asked for a group of only seven people. Are you likely to find some groups of seven people in which there is a match but other groups in which all seven people have different birth months? In the following exercises, you will estimate the probability that at least two people in a group of seven were born in the same month.

Exercises 1–4

1. What might be a good way to generate outcomes for the birth month problem—using coins, number cubes, cards, spinners, colored disks, or random numbers?

2. How would you simulate one trial of seven birth months?

3. How is a success determined for your simulation?

4. How is the simulated estimate determined for the probability that a least two in a group of seven people were born in the same month?

Lesson 11:   Conducting a Simulation to Estimate the Probability of an Event

Lesson Summary

To design a simulation:

- Identify the possible outcomes, and decide how to simulate them, using coins, number cubes, cards, spinners, colored disks, or random numbers.

- Specify what a trial for the simulation will look like and what a success and a failure would mean.

- Make sure you carry out enough trials to ensure that the estimated probability gets closer to the actual probability as you do more trials. There is no need for a specific number of trials at this time; however, you want to make sure to carry out enough trials so that the relative frequencies level off.

Name _____   Date _____

Liang wants to form a chess club. His principal says that he can do that if Liang can find six players, including himself. How would you conduct a simulated model that estimates the probability that Liang will find at least five other players to join the club if he asks eight players who have a 70% chance of agreeing to join the club? Suggest a simulation model for Liang by describing how you would do the following parts.

a. Specify the device you want to use to simulate one person being asked.

b. What outcome(s) of the device would represent the person agreeing to be a member?

c. What constitutes a trial using your device in this problem?

d. What constitutes a success using your device in this problem?

e. Based on 50 trials, using the method you have suggested, how would you calculate the estimate for the probability that Liang will be able to form a chess club?

1. George typically takes 6 free throws during one basketball game. Usually, George makes 80% of his free throw shots. Design a simulation to estimate the probability that George will make at least 4 free throws during his next game.

    a. How would you simulate the number of free throws George makes and misses?

        I could put 10 slips of paper in a bag, 8 of them labeled M, for a made shot, and 2 of them labeled L, for a missed shot.

        > I can do this in more than one way but would have to have either 5 or 10 possible outcomes since 80% represents $\frac{8}{10}$, or $\frac{4}{5}$.

    b. What constitutes a trial for this simulation?

        A trial for this simulation would be picking 6 pieces of paper from the bag, replacing each piece of paper before picking again.

        > Each piece of paper represents one shot.

    c. What constitutes a success in a trial in this problem?

        A success would be looking at the 6 pieces of paper that were picked and seeing 4 or more papers that say "made."

        > A success is a simulation where the results show George making 4 or more free throws.

    d. Carry out 12 trials, list your results, and compute an estimate of the probability that George will make at least 4 of his free throw shots.

        > I will refer back to part (b) to remember what a trial consists of and repeat this 12 times.

MMMLML	*LMLLMM*	*MMLMMM*
LMLLMM	*LMMMMM*	*LMLMMM*
MLLMMM	*MMLMLL*	*MMMMMM*
MMLMMM	*LLMLMM*	*MMMLMM*

        > 8 of the 12 trials show at least four made (M) shots.

        $$\frac{8}{12} = \frac{2}{3}$$

1. A model airplane has two engines. It can fly if one engine fails but is in serious trouble if both engines fail. The engines function independently of one another. On any given flight, the probability of a failure is 0.10 for each engine. Design a simulation to estimate the probability that the airplane will be in serious trouble the next time it goes up.

   a. How would you simulate the status of an engine?

   b. What constitutes a trial for this simulation?

   c. What constitutes a success for this simulation?

   d. Carry out 50 trials of your simulation, list your results, and calculate an estimate of the probability that the airplane will be in serious trouble the next time it goes up.

2. In an effort to increase sales, a cereal manufacturer created a really neat toy that has six parts to it. One part is put into each box of cereal. Which part is in a box is not known until the box is opened. You can play with the toy without having all six parts, but it is better to have the complete set. If you are really lucky, you might only need to buy six boxes to get a complete set. But if you are very unlucky, you might need to buy many, many boxes before obtaining all six parts.

   a. How would you represent the outcome of purchasing a box of cereal, keeping in mind that there are six different parts? There is one part in each box.

   b. If it was stated that a customer would have to buy at least 10 boxes of cereal to collect all six parts, what constitutes a trial in this problem?

   c. What constitutes a success in a trial in this problem?

   d. Carry out 15 trials, list your results, and compute an estimate of the probability that it takes the purchase of 10 or more boxes to get all six parts.

3. Suppose that a type A blood donor is needed for a certain surgery. Carry out a simulation to answer the following question: If 40% of donors have type A blood, what is an estimate of the probability that it will take at least four donors to find one with type A blood?

   a. How would you simulate a blood donor having or not having type A?

   b. What constitutes a trial for this simulation?

   c. What constitutes a success for this simulation?

   d. Carry out 15 trials, list your results, and compute an estimate for the probability that it takes at least four donors to find one with type A blood.

Example 1: Number Cube

Your teacher gives you a number cube with numbers 1–6 on its faces. You have never seen that particular cube before. You are asked to state a theoretical probability model for rolling it once. A probability model consists of the list of possible outcomes (the sample space) and the theoretical probabilities associated with each of the outcomes. You say that the probability model might assign a probability of $\frac{1}{6}$ to each of the possible outcomes, but because you have never seen this particular cube before, you would like to roll it a few times. (Maybe it is a trick cube.) Suppose your teacher allows you to roll it 500 times, and you get the following results:

Outcome	1	2	3	4	5	6
Frequency	77	92	75	90	76	90

Exercises 1–2

1. If the equally likely model was correct, about how many of each outcome would you expect to see if the cube is rolled 500 times?

2. Based on the data from the 500 rolls, how often were odd numbers observed? How often were even numbers observed?

Example 2: Probability Model

Two black balls and two white balls are put in a small cup whose bottom allows the four balls to fit snugly. After shaking the cup well, two patterns of colors are possible, as shown. The pattern on the left shows the similar colors are opposite each other, and the pattern on the right shows the similar colors are next to or adjacent to each other.

Philippe is asked to specify a probability model for the chance experiment of shaking the cup and observing the pattern. He thinks that because there are two outcomes—like heads and tails on a coin—that the outcomes should be equally likely. Sylvia isn't so sure that the equally likely model is correct, so she would like to collect some data before deciding on a model.

Exercise 3

3. Collect data for Sylvia. Carry out the experiment of shaking a cup that contains four balls, two black and two white, observing, and recording whether the pattern is opposite or adjacent. Repeat this process 20 times. Then, combine the data with those collected by your classmates.

   Do your results agree with Philippe's equally likely model, or do they indicate that Sylvia had the right idea? Explain.

Exercises 4–5

There are three popular brands of mixed nuts. Your teacher loves cashews, and in his experience of having purchased these brands, he suggests that not all brands have the same percentage of cashews. One has around 20% cashews, one has 25%, and one has 35%.

Your teacher has bags labeled A, B, and C representing the three brands. The bags contain red beads representing cashews and brown beads representing other types of nuts. One bag contains 20% red beads, another 25% red beads, and the third has 35% red beads. You are to determine which bag contains which percentage of cashews. You cannot just open the bags and count the beads.

4. Work as a class to design a simulation. You need to agree on what an outcome is, what a trial is, what a success is, and how to calculate the estimated probability of getting a cashew. Base your estimate on 50 trials.

5. Your teacher will give your group one of the bags labeled A, B, or C. Using your plan from part (a), collect your data. Do you think you have the 20%, 25%, or 35% cashews bag? Explain.

Exercises 6–8

Suppose you have two bags, A and B, in which there are an equal number of slips of paper. Positive numbers are written on the slips. The numbers are not known, but they are whole numbers between 1 and 75, inclusive. The same number may occur on more than one slip of paper in a bag.

These bags are used to play a game. In this game, you choose one of the bags and then choose one slip from that bag. If you choose Bag A and the number you choose from it is a prime number, then you win. If you choose Bag B and the number you choose from it is a power of 2, you win. Which bag should you choose?

6. Emma suggests that it does not matter which bag you choose because you do not know anything about what numbers are inside the bags. So, she thinks that you are equally likely to win with either bag. Do you agree with her? Explain.

7. Aamir suggests that he would like to collect some data from both bags before making a decision about whether or not the model is equally likely. Help Aamir by drawing 50 slips from each bag, being sure to replace each one before choosing again. Each time you draw a slip, record whether it would have been a winner or not. Using the results, what is your estimate for the probability of drawing a prime number from Bag A and drawing a power of 2 from Bag B?

8. If you were to play this game, which bag would you choose? Explain why you would pick this bag.

EUREKA MATH®

Name _____ Date _____

There are four pieces of bubble gum left in a quarter machine. Two are red, and two are yellow. Chandra puts two quarters in the machine. One piece is for her, and one is for her friend, Kay. If the two pieces are the same color, she is happy because they will not have to decide who gets what color. Chandra claims that they are equally likely to get the same color because the colors are either the same or they are different. Check her claim by doing a simulation.

a. Name a device that can be used to simulate getting a piece of bubble gum. Specify what outcome of the device represents a red piece and what outcome represents yellow.

b. Define what a trial is for your simulation.

c. Define what constitutes a success in a trial of your simulation.

d. Perform and list 50 simulated trials. Based on your results, is Chandra's equally likely model correct?

A recall has been issued for one type of small toy car and one type of large toy car because so many of the cars have small pieces breaking off.

Brett believed that the probability of having a large toy car that was recalled is bigger than the probability of having a small toy car that was recalled because the large toy car would have more parts that could break. However, Rachel believed that the probability of having a recalled large toy car is the same as having a recalled small toy car.

a. Simulate inspecting a small toy car by pulling a single card from a standard 52-card deck of cards. Let a heart simulate a recalled small toy car and all other cards simulate a safe small toy car. Do 50 trials, and compute an estimate of the probability that a small toy car is recalled.

> In order to have an accurate estimated probability, I replace each card before picking a new one.

Students pick 50 cards (replacing them each time) and record the results. Students then identify the number of hearts chosen out of the 50 trials. Since hearts represent $\frac{1}{4}$ of a standard 52-card deck, the estimated probability should be close to $\frac{1}{4}$.

b. Simulate inspecting a large toy car by pulling a single card from a standard 52-card deck of cards. Let a black face card simulate a recalled large toy car and all other cards simulate a safe large toy car. Do 50 trials, and compute an estimate of the probability that a large toy car is recalled.

> I know a face card is a Jack, Queen, or King.

Students again pick 50 cards (replacing them each time) and record the results. Students then identify the number of black face cards chosen out of the 50 trials. Since black face cards represent $\frac{6}{52}$, or $\frac{3}{26}$, of the deck of cards, the estimated probability should be close to $\frac{3}{26}$.

c. For this problem, suppose that the two simulations provide accurate estimates of the probability of a recalled small toy car and a recalled large toy car. Compare your two probability estimates, and decide whether Brett's or Rachel's belief was more reasonable than the other. Explain your reasoning.

Neither person had the correct idea. The probability of having a recalled small toy car was greater than the probability of having a recalled large toy car.

> Although the estimates will be different, there is a greater chance of picking a heart than a black face card from a deck of cards. Therefore, I know that it is more likely to have a greater probability in part (a) than in part (b).

1. Some M&M's® are "defective." For example, a defective M&M® may have its *M* missing, or it may be cracked, broken, or oddly shaped. Is the probability of getting a defective M&M® higher for peanut M&M's® than for plain M&M's®?

   Gloriann suggests the probability of getting a defective plain M&M® is the same as the probability of getting a defective peanut M&M®. Suzanne does not think this is correct because a peanut M&M® is bigger than a plain M&M®, and therefore has a greater opportunity to be damaged.

   a. Simulate inspecting a plain M&M® by rolling two number cubes. Let a sum of 7 or 11 represent a defective plain M&M® and the other possible rolls represent a plain M&M® that is not defective. Do 50 trials, and compute an estimate of the probability that a plain M&M® is defective. Record the 50 outcomes you observed. Explain your process.

   b. Simulate inspecting a peanut M&M® by selecting a card from a well-shuffled deck of cards. Let a one-eyed face card and clubs represent a defective peanut M&M® and the other cards represent a peanut M&M® that is not defective. Be sure to replace the chosen card after each trial and to shuffle the deck well before choosing the next card. Note that the one-eyed face cards are the king of diamonds, jack of hearts, and jack of spades. Do 20 trials, and compute an estimate of the probability that a peanut M&M® is defective. Record the list of 20 cards that you observed. Explain your process.

   c. For this problem, suppose that the two simulations provide accurate estimates of the probability of a defective M&M® for plain and peanut M&M's®. Compare your two probability estimates, and decide whether Gloriann's belief is reasonable that the defective probability is the same for both types of M&M's®. Explain your reasoning.

2. One at a time, mice are placed at the start of the maze shown below. There are four terminal stations at A, B, C, and D. At each point where a mouse has to decide in which direction to go, assume that it is equally likely for it to choose any of the possible directions. A mouse cannot go backward.

In the following simulated trials, L stands for left, R for right, and S for straight. Estimate the probability that a mouse finds station C where the food is. No food is at A, B, or D. The following data were collected on 50 simulated paths that the mice took.

LR RL RL LL LS LS RL RR RR RL

RL LR LR RR LR LR LL LS RL LR

RR LS RL RR RL LR LR LL LS RR

RL RL RL RR RR RR LR LL LL RR

RR LS RR LR RR RR LL RR LS LS

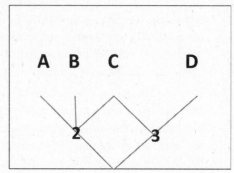

a. What paths constitute a success, and what paths constitute a failure?

b. Use the data to estimate the probability that a mouse finds food. Show your calculation.

c. Paige suggests that it is equally likely that a mouse gets to any of the four terminal stations. What does your simulation suggest about whether her equally likely model is believable? If it is not believable, what do your data suggest is a more believable model?

d. Does your simulation support the following theoretical probability model? Explain.

   i.   The probability a mouse finds terminal point A is 0.167.

   ii.   The probability a mouse finds terminal point B is 0.167.

   iii. The probability a mouse finds terminal point C is 0.417.

   iv.   The probability a mouse finds terminal point D is 0.250.

Lesson 12:   Applying Probability to Make Informed Decisions

EUREKA
MATH

In this lesson, you will learn about collecting data from a sample that is selected from a population. You will also learn about summary values for both a population and a sample and think about what can be learned about the population by looking at a sample from that population.

Exercises 1–4: Collecting Data

1. Describe what you would do if you had to collect data to investigate the following statistical questions using either a sample statistic or a population characteristic. Explain your reasoning in each case.

   a. How might you collect data to answer the question, "Does the soup taste good?"

   b. How might you collect data to answer the question, "How many movies do students in your class see in a month?"

   c. How might you collect data to answer the question, "What is the median price of a home in our town?"

   d. How might you collect data to answer the question, "How many pets do people own in my neighborhood?"

   e. How might you collect data to answer the question, "What is the typical number of absences in math classes at your school on a given day?"

f.   How might you collect data to answer the question, "What is the typical life span of a particular brand of flashlight battery?"

g.   How might you collect data to answer the question, "What percentage of girls and of boys in your school have a curfew?"

h.   How might you collect data to answer the question, "What is the most common blood type of students in my class?"

A population is the entire set of objects (e.g., people, animals, and plants) from which data might be collected. A *sample* is a subset of the population. Numerical summary values calculated using data from an entire population are called *population characteristics*. Numerical summary values calculated using data from a sample are called *statistics*.

2.   For which of the scenarios in Exercise 1 did you describe collecting data from a population and which from a sample?

3.   Think about collecting data in the scenarios above. Give at least two reasons you might want to collect data from a sample rather than from the entire population.

EUREKA MATH

4. Make up a result you might get in response to the situations in Exercise 1, and identify whether the result would be based on a population characteristic or a sample statistic.

    a. Does the soup taste good?

    b. How many movies do students in your class see in a month?

    c. What is the median price of a home in our town?

    d. How many pets do people own in my neighborhood?

    e. What is the typical number of absences in math classes at your school on a given day?

    f. What is the typical life span of a particular brand of flashlight battery?

    g. What percentage of girls and of boys in your school have a curfew?

    h. What is the most common blood type of students in my class?

Exercise 5: Population or Sample?

5. Indicate whether the following statements are summarizing data collected to answer a statistical question from a population or from a sample. Identify references in the statement as population characteristics or sample statistics.

a. 54% of the responders to a poll at a university indicated that wealth needed to be distributed more evenly among people.

b. Are students in the Bay Shore School District proficient on the state assessments in mathematics? In 2013, after all the tests taken by the students in the Bay Shore schools were evaluated, over 52% of those students were at or above proficient on the state assessment.

c. Does talking on mobile phones while driving distract people? Researchers measured the reaction times of 38 study participants as they talked on mobile phones and found that the average level of distraction from their driving was rated 2.25 out of 5.

d. Did most people living in New York in 2010 have at least a high school education? Based on the data collected from all New York residents in 2010 by the U.S. Census Bureau, 84.6% of people living in New York had at least a high school education.

e. Were there more deaths than births in the United States between July 2011 and July 2012? Data from a health service agency indicated that there were 2% more deaths than births in the United States during that time frame.

Lesson 13:   Populations, Samples, and Generalizing from
a Sample to a Population

f. What is the fifth best-selling book in the United States? Based on the sales of books in the United States, the fifth best-selling book was *Oh, the Places You'll Go!* by Dr. Seuss.

Exercises 6–8: A Census

6. When data are collected from an entire population, it is called a *census*. The United States takes a census of its population every ten years, with the most recent one occurring in 2010. Go to http://www.census.gov to find the history of the U.S. census.

    a. Identify three things that you found to be interesting.

    b. Why is the census important in the United States?

7. Go to the site: www.census.gov/2010census/popmap/ipmtext.php?fl=36.
    Select the state of New York.

    a. How many people were living in New York for the 2010 census?

    b. Estimate the ratio of those 65 and older to those under 18 years old. Why is this important to think about?

    c. Is the ratio a population characteristic or a statistic? Explain your thinking.

8. The American Community Survey (ACS) takes samples from a small percentage of the U.S. population in years
    between the censuses. (www.census.gov/acs/www/about_the_survey/american_community_survey/)

    a. What is the difference between the way the ACS collects information about the U.S. population and the way
        the U.S. Census Bureau collects information?

    b. In 2011, the ACS sampled workers living in New York about commuting to work each day. Why do you think
        these data are important for the state to know?

    c. Suppose that from a sample of 200,000 New York workers, 32,400 reported traveling more than an hour to
        work each day. From this information, statisticians determined that between 16% and 16.4% of the workers
        in the state traveled more than an hour to work every day in 2011. If there were 8,437,512 workers in the
        entire population, about how many traveled more than an hour to work each day?

    d. Reasoning from a sample to the population is called *making an inference* about a population characteristic.
        Identify the statistic involved in making the inference in part (c).

    e. The data about traveling time to work suggest that across the United States typically between 79.8% and 80%
        of commuters travel alone, 10% to 10.2% carpool, and 4.9% to 5.1% use public transportation. Survey your
        classmates to find out how a worker in their families gets to work. How do the results compare to the national
        data? What might explain any differences?

Lesson Summary

When data from a population are used to calculate a numerical summary, the value is called a *population characteristic*. When data from a sample are used to calculate a numerical summary, the value is called a *sample statistic*. Sample statistics can be used to learn about population characteristics.

The History of the U.S. Census

The word *census* is Latin in origin and means to tax. The first U.S. census took place over 200 years ago, but the United States is certainly not the first country to implement a census. Based on archaeological records, it appears that the ancient Egyptians conducted a census as early as 3000 B.C.E.

The U.S. census is mandated by the U.S. Constitution in Article I, Section 2, which states, in part, "Representatives and direct Taxes shall be apportioned among the several States ... according to their respective Numbers .... The Number of Representatives shall not exceed one for every thirty thousand, but each State shall have at Least one Representative ...." The Constitution then specifies how to calculate the number of people in each state and how often the census should take place.

The U.S. census has been conducted every ten years since 1790, but as time has passed, our census has evolved. Not only have the types of questions changed but also the manner in which the data are collected and tabulated. Originally, the census had only a few questions, the purpose of which was to discern the number of people in each household and their ages. Presumably, these data were used to determine the number of men in each state who were available to go to war. Federal marshals were charged with the task of conducting this first census. After collecting data from their respective jurisdictions, the marshals sent the data to President Washington.

As time has passed, more questions have been added to the U.S. census. Today, the census includes questions designed to collect data in various fields such as manufacturing, commerce, and transportation, to name a few. Data that were once manually tabulated are now processed by computers. Home visits by census officials were once the norm, but now the census is conducted primarily through the U.S. Postal Service. Each household in the United States receives in the mail a copy of the census questionnaire to be completed by its head of household who then mails it back to the Census Bureau. Home visits are paid only to those individuals who do not return the questionnaire by the specified deadline.

The census is an important part of our Constitution. Today, the census not only tells us the population of each state, thereby determining the number of representatives that each state will have in the House of Representatives, but it also provides the U.S. government with very useful data that paint a picture of the current state of our population and how it has changed over the decades.

"U.S. Census History," *essortment*, accessed November 4, 2014, http://www.essortment.com/census-history-20901.html.

Name _____   Date _____

What is the difference between a population characteristic and a sample statistic? Give an example to support your answer. Clearly identify the population and sample in your example.

1. For each of the following questions: (1) Describe how you would collect data to answer the question, and (2) decide whether it would result in a sample statistic or a population characteristic.

    a.   How many pets do people own in my class?

    > I am able to collect data from the entire population because the population size is small.

    (1) *I can provide all students in my class a slip of paper and have them write the number of pets they have on the piece of paper.*

    (2) *The result would be a population characteristic because I would be gathering data from the entire population (my class).*

    > There are too many people in my city to collect data from everyone, so I only collect data from a sample.

    b.   How many pets do people own in my city?

    (1) *I can stand outside a grocery store and ask customers as they enter the store how many pets they own.*

    (2) *The result would be a sample statistic because I would be gathering information from only a small subset of the entire population (my city).*

2. Identify a question that would lead to collecting data from the given set as a population and one where the data could be a sample from a larger population.

    a.   The entire seventh grade

    The entire seventh grade could be a population when determining the number of seventh grade student absences on a given day.

    > Data that could be collected easily, maybe from a computer, can be collected from an entire population.

    The entire seventh grade could be a sample when determining the number of hours a middle school student sleeps on a school night.

    > I would want to collect data that can be summarized from a sample to generalize to the population.

Lesson 13:   Populations, Samples, and Generalizing from
             a Sample to a Population

© 2019 Great Minds®. eureka-math.org

b.   The entire school district

I know answers will vary for this type of problem.

The entire school district might be a population when determining math scores on the state assessment for the district.

The entire school district might be a sample when determining the median family income in the state.

1. The lunch program at Blake Middle School is being revised to align with the new nutritional standards that reduce calories and increase servings of fruits and vegetables. The administration decided to do a census of all students at Blake Middle School by giving a survey to all students about the school lunches.

   a. Name some questions that you would include in the survey. Explain why you think those questions would be important to ask.

   b. Read through the paragraph below that describes some of the survey results. Then, identify the population characteristics and the sample statistics.

   > About $\frac{3}{4}$ of the students surveyed eat the school lunch regularly. The median number of days per month that students at Blake Middle School ate a school lunch was 18 days. 36% of students responded that their favorite fruit is bananas. The survey results for Tanya's seventh-grade homeroom showed that the median number of days per month that her classmates ate lunch at school was 22, and only 20% liked bananas. The fiesta salad was approved by 78% of the group of students who tried it, but when it was put on the lunch menu, only 40% of the students liked it. Of the seventh graders as a whole, 73% liked spicy jicama strips, but only 2 out of 5 of all the middle school students liked them.

2. For each of the following questions, (1) describe how you would collect data to answer the question, and (2) describe whether it would result in a sample statistic or a population characteristic.

   a. Where should the eighth-grade class go for its class trip?

   b. What is the average number of pets per family for families that live in your town?

   c. If people tried a new diet, what percentage would have an improvement in cholesterol reading?

   d. What is the average grade point of students who got accepted to a particular state university?

   e. What is a typical number of home runs hit in a particular season for major league baseball players?

3. Identify a question that would lead to collecting data from the given set as a population and a question where the data could be a sample from a larger population.

   a. All students in your school

   b. Your state

4. Suppose that researchers sampled attendees of a certain movie and found that the mean age was 17 years old. Based on this observation, which of the following would be most likely?

   a. The mean age of all of the people who went to see the movie was 17 years old.

   b. About a fourth of the people who went to see the movie were older than 51.

   c. The mean age of all people who went to see the movie would probably be in an interval around 17 years of age, that is, between 15 and 19.

   d. The median age of those who attended the movie was 17 years old as well.

5. The headlines proclaimed: "Education Impacts Work-Life Earnings Five Times More Than Other Demographic Factors, Census Bureau Reports." According to a U.S. Census Bureau study, education levels had more effect on earnings over a 40-year span in the workforce than any other demographic factor.
www.census.gov/newsroom/releases/archives/education/cb11-153.html

a. The article stated that the estimated impact on annual earnings between a professional degree and an eighth-grade education was roughly five times the impact of gender, which was $13,000. What would the difference in annual earnings be with a professional degree and with an eighth-grade education?

b. Explain whether you think the data are from a population or a sample, and identify either the population characteristic or the sample statistic.

              Populations, Samples, and Generalizing from
                                a Sample to a Population

EUREKA
MATH

As you learned in Lesson 13, sampling is a central concept in statistics. Examining every element in a population is usually impossible. So, research and articles in the media typically refer to a "sample" from a population. In this lesson, you will begin to think about how to choose a sample.

Exercises 1–2: What Is Random?

1. Write down a sequence of heads/tails you think would typically occur if you tossed a coin 20 times. Compare your sequence to the ones written by some of your classmates. How are they alike? How are they different?

2. Working with a partner, toss a coin 20 times, and write down the sequence of heads and tails you get.

   a. Compare your results with your classmates'.

   b. How are your results from actually tossing the coin different from the sequences you and your classmates wrote down?

c.   Toni claimed she could make up a set of numbers that would be random. What would you say to her?

Exercises 3–11: Length of Words in the Poem "Casey at the Bat"

3.   Suppose you wanted to learn about the lengths of the words in the poem "Casey at the Bat." You plan to select a sample of eight words from the poem and use these words to answer the following statistical question: On average, how long is a word in the poem? What is the population of interest here?

4.   Look at the poem "Casey at the Bat" by Ernest Thayer, and select eight words you think are representative of words in the poem. Record the number of letters in each word you selected. Find the mean number of letters in the words you chose.

5.   A random sample is a sample in which every possible sample of the same size has an equal chance of being chosen. Do you think the set of words you wrote down was random? Why or why not?

6.   Working with a partner, follow your teacher's instructions for randomly choosing eight words. Begin with the title of the poem, and count a hyphenated word as one word.

a.   Record the eight words you randomly selected, and find the mean number of letters in those words.

EUREKA MATH

b.   Compare the mean of your random sample to the mean you found in Exercise 4. Explain how you found the mean for each sample.

7.   As a class, compare the means from Exercise 4 and the means from Exercise 6. Your teacher will provide a chart to compare the means. Record your mean from Exercise 4 and your mean for Exercise 6 on this chart.

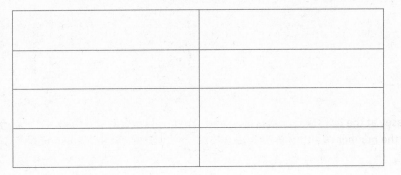

8.   Do you think the means from Exercise 4 or the means from Exercise 6 are more representative of the mean of all of the words in the poem? Explain your choice.

9.   The actual mean of the words in the poem "Casey at the Bat" is 4.2 letters. Based on the fact that the population mean is 4.2 letters, are the means from Exercise 4 or means from Exercise 6 a better representation of the mean of the population? Explain your answer.

10. How did the population mean of 4.2 letters compare to the mean of your random sample from Exercise 6 and to the mean you found in Exercise 4?

11. Summarize how you would estimate the mean number of letters in the words of another poem based on what you learned in the above exercises.

Lesson 14:   Selecting a Sample

EUREKA MATH®

\1\ Casey at the Bat

The Outlook wasn't brilliant for the Mudville nine that day: The score stood four to two, \2\ with but one inning more to play. And then when Cooney died at first, and Barrows did the same, A \3\ sickly silence fell upon the patrons of the game.

A straggling few got up to go in deep despair. The \4\ rest Clung to that hope which springs eternal in the human breast; They thought, if only Casey could get but \5\ a whack at that—We'd put up even money, now, with Casey at the bat.

But Flynn preceded Casey, as \6\ did also Jimmy Blake, And the former was a lulu and the latter was a cake; So upon that stricken \7\ multitude grim melancholy sat, For there seemed but little chance of Casey's getting to the bat.

But Flynn let drive \8\ a single, to the wonderment of all, And Blake, the much despised, tore the cover off the ball; And when \9\ the dust had lifted, and the men saw what had occurred, There was Jimmy safe at second and Flynn a \10\ hugging third.

Then from five thousand throats and more there rose a lusty yell; It rumbled through the valley, it \11\ rattled in the dell; It knocked upon the mountain and recoiled upon the flat, For Casey, mighty Casey, was advancing \12\ to the bat.

There was ease in Casey's manner as he stepped into his place; There was pride in Casey's \13\ bearing and a smile on Casey's face. And when, responding to the cheers, he lightly doffed his hat, No stranger \14\ in the crowd could doubt 'twas Casey at the bat.

Ten thousand eyes were on him as he rubbed his \15\ hands with dirt; Five thousand tongues applauded when he wiped them on his shirt. Then while the writhing pitcher ground \16\ the ball into his hip, Defiance gleamed in Casey's eye, a sneer curled Casey's lip.

And now the leather covered \17\ sphere came hurtling through the air, And Casey stood a-watching it in haughty grandeur there. Close by the sturdy batsman \18\ the ball unheeded sped—"That ain't my style," said Casey. "Strike one," the umpire said.

From the benches, black with \19\ people, there went up a muffled roar, Like the beating of the storm waves on a stern and distant shore. \20\ "Kill him! Kill the umpire!" shouted someone on the stand; And it's likely they'd a-killed him had not Casey raised \21\ his hand.

With a smile of Christian charity great Casey's visage shone; He stilled the rising tumult; he bade the **\22** game go on; He signaled to the pitcher, and once more the spheroid flew; But Casey still ignored it, and **\23**the umpire said, "Strike two."

"Fraud!" cried the maddened thousands, and echo answered fraud; But one scornful look from Casey **\24** and the audience was awed. They saw his face grow stern and cold, they saw his muscles strain, And they **\25** knew that Casey wouldn't let that ball go by again.

The sneer is gone from Casey's lip, his teeth are **\26** clenched in hate; He pounds with cruel violence his bat upon the plate. And now the pitcher holds the ball, **\27** and now he lets it go, And now the air is shattered by the force of Casey's blow.

Oh, somewhere **\28** in this favored land the sun is shining bright; The band is playing somewhere, and somewhere hearts are light, And **\29** somewhere men are laughing, and somewhere children shout; But there is no joy in Mudville—mighty Casey has struck out.

by Ernest Lawrence Thayer

EUREKA MATH

Name _____ Date _____

Write down three things you learned about taking a sample from the work we have done today.

1. Would any of the following provide a random sample of the length of words in a children's book? If not, explain.

   a. Placing all the words in a bag and picking a sample of words from the bag

      This method would provide a random sample.

      > If I use a method to find a sample, it eliminates the randomness and is not a random sample.

   b. Finding the length of the last word on each page of the book

      This would not be a random sample because the book may be a rhyming book, which would make the last words on each page similar to each other and maybe not a good representation of the other words in the book.

2. Indicate whether the following are random samples from the given population, and explain why or why not.

   a. Population: All families in the city; sample includes people sitting at one bus stop.

      No, because the sample only includes people in one part of the city and only people who ride the bus.

      > This sample only includes a specific group of people from my city.

   b. Population: Teachers at a school; sample selected by putting names into a bowl and drawing the sample from the bowl.

      Yes, all the teachers have the same opportunity to be chosen.

3. What questions about the samples and populations might you want to ask if you saw the following headlines in a newspaper?

   a. Soccer is the new favorite sport of children!

      > Answers may vary.

      How many people were interviewed? Was the survey conducted at a soccer field?

      > I have to think of ways that a biased sample may have been chosen.

   b. Spicy Mint Gum is favored by 80% of consumers.

      What were the other choices? How many people were surveyed?

Lesson 14:   Selecting a Sample   **173**

1. Would any of the following provide a random sample of letters used in the text of the book *Harry Potter and the Sorcerer's Stone* by J.K. Rowling? Explain your reasoning.

   a. Use the first letter of every word of a randomly chosen paragraph.

   b. Number all of the letters in the words in a paragraph of the book, cut out the numbers, and put them in a bag. Then, choose a random set of numbers from the bag to identify which letters you will use.

   c. Have a family member or friend write down a list of his favorite words, and count the number of times each of the letters occurs.

2. Indicate whether the following are random samples from the given population, and explain why or why not.

   a. Population: All students in school; the sample includes every fifth student in the hall outside of class.

   b. Population: Students in your class; the sample consists of students who have the letter *s* in their last names.

   c. Population: Students in your class; the sample is selected by putting their names in a hat and drawing the sample from the hat.

   d. Population: People in your neighborhood; the sample includes those outside in the neighborhood at 6:00 p.m.

   e. Population: Everyone in a room; the sample is selected by having everyone toss a coin, and those that result in heads are the sample.

3. Consider the two sample distributions of the number of letters in randomly selected words shown below:

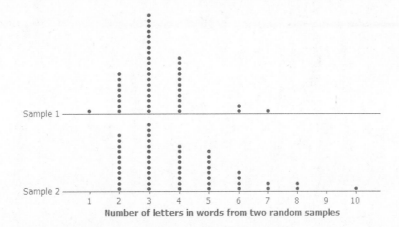

   a. Describe each distribution using statistical terms as much as possible.

   b. Do you think the two samples came from the same poem? Why or why not?

4. What questions about samples and populations might you want to ask if you saw the following headlines in a newspaper?

   a. "Peach Pop is the top flavor according to 8 out of 10 people."

   b. "Candidate X looks like a winner! 10 out of 12 people indicate they will vote for Candidate X."

   c. "Students overworked. Over half of 400 people surveyed think students spend too many hours on homework."

   d. "Action/adventure was selected as the favorite movie type by an overwhelming 75% of those surveyed."

In this lesson, you will investigate taking random samples and how random samples from the same population vary.

Exercises 1–5: Sampling Pennies

1. Do you think different random samples from the same population will be fairly similar? Explain your reasoning.

2. The plot below shows the number of years since being minted (the penny age) for 150 pennies that JJ had collected over the past year. Describe the shape, center, and spread of the distribution.

Dot Plot of Population of Penny Ages

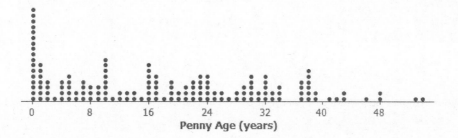

3. Place ten dots on the number line that you think might be the distribution of a sample of 10 pennies from the jar.

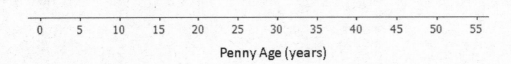

Penny Age (years)

4. Select a random sample of 10 pennies, and make a dot plot of the ages. Describe the distribution of the penny ages in your sample. How does it compare to the population distribution?

5. Compare your sample distribution to the sample distributions on the board.

    a. What do you observe?

    b. How does your sample distribution compare to those on the board?

Exercises 6–9: Grocery Prices and Rounding

6. Look over some of the grocery prices for this activity. Consider the following statistical question: "Do the store owners price the merchandise with cents that are closer to a higher dollar value or a lower dollar value?" Describe a plan that might answer that question that does not involve working with all 100 items.

EUREKA MATH

7. Do the store owners price the merchandise with cents that are closer to a higher dollar value or a lower dollar value? To investigate this question in one situation, you will look at some grocery prices in weekly flyers and advertising for local grocery stores.

   a. How would you round $3.49 and $4.99 to the nearest dollar?

   b. If the advertised price was three for $4.35, how much would you expect to pay for one item?

   c. Do you think more grocery prices will round up or round down? Explain your thinking.

8. Follow your teacher's instructions to cut out the items and their prices from the weekly flyers and put them in a bag. Select a random sample of 25 items without replacement, and record the items and their prices in the table below.

Item	Price	Rounded	Item	Price	Rounded

Example of chart suggested:

Student	Number of Times the Prices Were Rounded to the Higher Value	Percent of Prices Rounded Up	Number of Times the Prices Were Rounded to the Lower Value
Bettina	20	80%	5

9. Round each of the prices in your sample to the nearest dollar, and count the number of times you rounded up and the number of times you rounded down.

   a. Given the results of your sample, how would you answer the question: Are grocery prices in the weekly ads at the local grocery closer to a higher dollar value or a lower dollar value?

   b. Share your results with classmates who used the same flyer or ads. Looking at the results of several different samples, how would you answer the question in part (a)?

   c. Identify the population, sample, and sample statistic used to answer the statistical question.

   d. Bettina says that over half of all the prices in the grocery store will round up. What would you say to her?

100 Grocery Items (2013 prices)

T-bone steaks $6.99 (1 lb.)	Porterhouse steaks $7.29 (1 lb.)	Pasta sauce $2.19 (16 oz.)	Ice cream cups $7.29 (6 cups)
Hot dog buns $0.88 (6 buns)	Baking chips $2.99 (12 oz.)	Cheese chips $2.09 (12 oz.)	Cookies $1.77 (15 oz.)
Kidney beans $0.77 (15 oz.)	Box of oatmeal $1.77 (18 oz.)	Soup $0.77 (14 oz.)	Chicken breasts $7.77 (1.5 lb.)
Pancake syrup $2.99 (28 oz.)	Cranberry juice $2.77 (64 oz.)	Asparagus $3.29 (1 lb.)	Seedless cucumbers $1.29 (1 ct.)
Avocado $1.30 (1 ct.)	Sliced pineapple $2.99	Box of tea $4.29 (16 tea bags)	Cream cheese $2.77 (16 oz.)
Italian roll $1.39 (1 roll)	Turkey breast $4.99 (1 lb.)	Meatballs $5.79 (26 oz.)	Chili $1.35 (15 oz.)
Peanut butter $1.63 (12 oz.)	Green beans $0.99 (1 lb.)	Apples $1.99 (1 lb.)	Mushrooms $0.69 (8 oz.)
Brown sugar $1.29 (32 oz.)	Confectioners' sugar $1.39 (32 oz.)	Zucchini $0.79 (1 lb.)	Yellow onions $0.99 (1 lb.)
Green peppers $0.99 (1 ct.)	Mozzarella cheese $2.69 (8 oz.)	Frozen chicken $6.49 (48 oz.)	Olive oil $2.99 (17 oz.)
Dark chocolate $2.99 (9 oz.)	Cocoa mix $3.33 (1 package)	Margarine $1.48 (16 oz.)	Mac and cheese $0.66 (6-oz. box)
Birthday cake $9.49 (7 in.)	Crab legs $19.99 (1 lb.)	Sushi rolls $12.99 (20 ct.)	Prime rib $19.99 (4 lb.)
Cooked shrimp $12.99 (32 oz.)	Ice cream $4.49 (1 qt.)	Pork chops $1.79 (1 lb.)	Bananas $0.44 (1 lb.)

Chocolate milk $2.99 (1 gal.)	Beef franks $3.35 (1 lb.)	Sliced bacon $5.49 (1 lb.)	Fish fillets $6.29 (1 lb.)
Pears $1.29 (1 lb.)	Tangerines $3.99 (3 lb.)	Orange juice $2.98 (59 oz.)	Cherry pie $4.44 (8 in.)
Grapes $1.28 (1 lb.)	Peaches $1.28 (1 lb.)	Melon $1.69 (1 melon)	Tomatoes $1.49 (1 lb.)
Shredded cheese $1.88 (12 oz.)	Soda $0.88 (1 can)	Roast beef $6.49 (1 lb.)	Coffee $6.49 (1 lb.)
Feta cheese $4.99 (1 lb.)	Pickles $1.69 (12-oz. jar)	Loaf of rye bread $2.19	Crackers $2.69 (7.9 oz.)
Purified water $3.47 (35 pk.)	BBQ sauce $2.19 (24 oz.)	Ketchup $2.29 (34 oz.)	Chili sauce $1.77 (12 oz.)
Sugar $1.77 (5 lb.)	Flour $2.11 (4 lb.)	Breakfast cereal $2.79 (9 oz.)	Cane sugar $2.39 (4 lb.)
Cheese sticks $1.25 (10 oz.)	Cheese spread $2.49 (45 oz.)	Coffee creamer $2.99 (12 oz.)	Candy bars $7.77 (40 oz.)
Pudding mix $0.98 (6 oz.)	Fruit drink $1.11 (24 oz.)	Biscuit mix $0.89 (4 oz.)	Sausages $2.38 (13 oz.)
Ground beef $4.49 (1 lb.)	Apple juice $1.48 (64 oz.)	Ice cream sandwich $1.98 (12 ct.)	Cottage cheese $1.98 (24 oz.)
Frozen vegetables $0.88 (10 oz.)	English muffins $1.68 (6 ct.)	String cheese $6.09 (24 oz.)	Baby greens $2.98 (10 oz.)
Caramel apples $3.11 (1 ct.)	Pumpkin mix $3.50 (1 lb.)	Chicken salad $0.98 (2 oz.)	Whole wheat bread $1.55 (1 loaf)
Tuna $0.98 (2.5 oz.)	Nutrition bar $2.19 (1 bar)	Potato chips $2.39 (12 oz.)	2% milk $3.13 (1 gal.)

EUREKA MATH®

Name _____   Date _____

Identify each as true or false. Explain your reasoning in each case.

1. The values of a sample statistic for different random samples of the same size from the same population will be the same.

2. Random samples from the same population will vary from sample to sample.

3. If a random sample is chosen from a population that has a large cluster of points at the maximum, the sample is likely to have at least one element near the maximum.

Consider the distribution below:

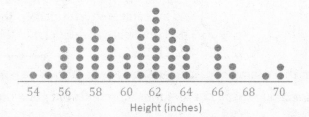

Height (inches)

1. What would you expect the distribution of a random sample size of 10 from the population look like?

   I would expect that a majority of the 10 data values will be between 56 inches and 64 inches, with maybe one data point smaller than 56 inches and two data points larger than 64 inches.

   > I know the sample should resemble the population, but there is more than one correct answer.

2. Random samples of different sizes that were selected from the population in Problem 1 are displayed below. How did your answer to Problem 1 compare to this sample size of 10?

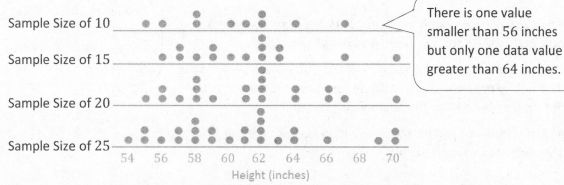

Height (inches)

> There is one value smaller than 56 inches but only one data value greater than 64 inches.

My expectation from Problem 1 closely matches the sample given in the first dot plot here.

> I notice that the dot plots are all similarly shaped. As the sample size gets larger, the dot plot looks even more like the dot plot of the population.

3. Why is it reasonable to think that these samples could have come from the above population?

   Each of the dot plots has a similar shape to the dot plot that represents the population.

4. Which of the box plots could represent a random sample from the distribution? Explain your thinking.

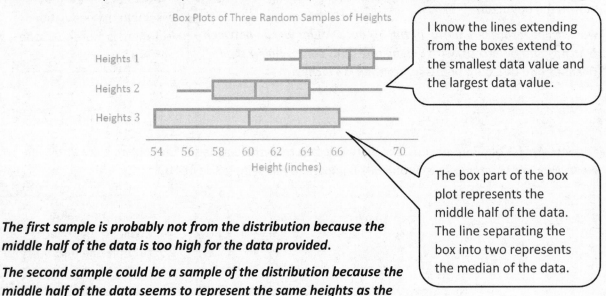

Box Plots of Three Random Samples of Heights

> I know the lines extending from the boxes extend to the smallest data value and the largest data value.

> The box part of the box plot represents the middle half of the data. The line separating the box into two represents the median of the data.

The first sample is probably not from the distribution because the middle half of the data is too high for the data provided.

The second sample could be a sample of the distribution because the middle half of the data seems to represent the same heights as the middle half of the data in the original distribution.

The third sample is not from the distribution because the range for the middle half of the data is too big.

Lesson 15:   Random Sampling

EUREKA MATH

1. Look at the distribution of years since the pennies were minted from Example 1. Which of the following box plots seem like they might not have come from a random sample from that distribution? Explain your thinking.

Box Plots of Three Random Samples of Penny Ages

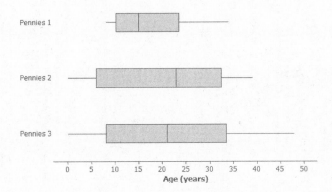

2. Given the following sample of scores on a physical fitness test, from which of the following populations might the sample have been chosen? Explain your reasoning.

Dot Plots of Four Populations and One Sample

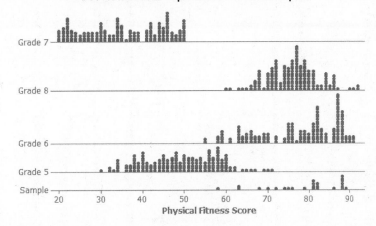

3. Consider the distribution below:

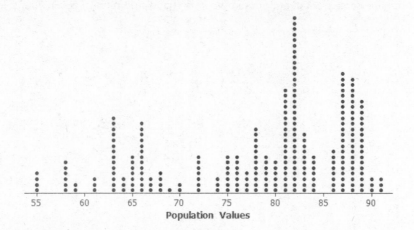

a. What would you expect the distribution of a random sample of size 10 from this population to look like?

b. Random samples of different sizes that were selected from the population in part (a) are displayed below. How did your answer to part (a) compare to these samples of size 10?

Dot Plots of Five Samples of Different Sizes

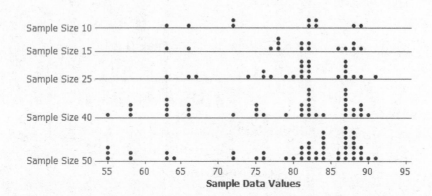

c. Why is it reasonable to think that these samples could have come from the above population?

d. What do you observe about the sample distributions as the sample size increases?

4. Based on your random sample of prices from Exercise 6, answer the following questions:

a. It looks like a lot of the prices end in 9. Do your sample results support that claim? Why or why not?

b. What is the typical price of the items in your sample? Explain how you found the price and why you chose that method.

EUREKA
MATH

5. The sample distributions of prices for three different random samples of 25 items from a grocery store are shown below.

   a. How do the distributions compare?

Dot Plots of Three Samples

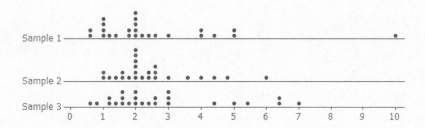

   b. Thomas says that if he counts the items in his cart at that grocery store and multiplies by $2.00, he will have a pretty good estimate of how much he will have to pay. What do you think of his strategy?

In this lesson, you will obtain random numbers to select a random sample. You will also design a plan for selecting a random sample to answer a statistical question about a population.

Example 1: Sampling Children's Books

What is the longest book you have ever read? *The Hobbit* has 95,022 words, and *The Cat in the Hat* has 830 words. Popular books vary in the number of words they have—not just the number of *different* words but the total number of words. The table below shows the total number of words in some of those books. The histogram displays the total number of words in 150 best-selling children's books with fewer than 100,000 words.

Book	Words	Book	Words	Book	Words
Black Beauty	59,635	Charlie and the Chocolate Factory	30,644	The Hobbit	95,022
The Catcher in the Rye	73,404	Old Yeller	35,968	Judy Moody Was in a Mood	11,049
The Adventures of Tom Sawyer	69,066	The Cat in the Hat	830	Treasure Island	66,950
The Secret Garden	80,398	Green Eggs and Ham	702	Magic Tree House Lions at Lunchtime	5,313
The Mouse and the Motorcycle	22,416	Little Bear	1,630	Harry Potter and the Sorcerer's Stone	77,325
The Wind in the Willows	58,424	The Red Badge of Courage	47,180	Harry Potter and the Chamber of Secrets	84,799
My Father's Dragon	7,682	Anne Frank: The Diary of a Young Girl	82,762	Junie B. Jones and the Stupid Smelly Bus	6,570
Frog and Toad All Year	1,727	Midnight for Charlie Bone	65,006	White Mountains	44,763
Book of Three	46,926	The Lion, The Witch and the Wardrobe	36,363	Double Fudge	38,860

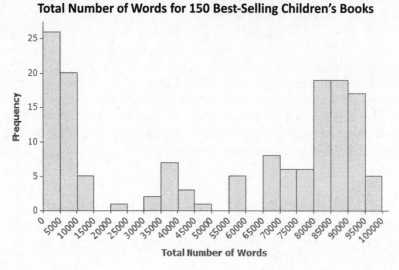

Exercises 1–2

1. From the table, choose two books with which you are familiar, and describe their locations in the data distribution shown in the histogram.

2. Put dots on the number line below that you think would represent a random sample of size 10 from the number of words distribution above.

Lesson 16:   Methods for Selecting a Random Sample

EUREKA MATH

Example 2: Using Random Numbers to Select a Sample

The histogram indicates the differences in the number of words in the collection of 150 books. How many words are typical for a best-selling children's book? Answering this question would involve collecting data, and there would be variability in those data. This makes the question a statistical question. Think about the 150 books used to create the histogram on the previous page as a population. How would you go about collecting data to determine the typical number of words for the books in this population?

How would you choose a random sample from the collection of 150 books discussed in this lesson?

The data for the number of words in the 150 best-selling children's books are listed below. Select a random sample of the number of words for 10 books.

Books 1–10	59,635	82,762	92,410	75,340	8,234	59,705	92,409	75,338	8,230	82,768
Books 11–20	73,404	65,006	88,250	2,100	81,450	72,404	88,252	2,099	81,451	65,011
Books 21–30	69,066	36,363	75,000	3,000	80,798	69,165	75,012	3,010	80,790	36,361
Books 31–40	80,398	95,022	71,200	3,250	81,450	80,402	71,198	3,252	81,455	95,032
Books 41–50	22,416	11,049	81,400	3,100	83,475	22,476	81,388	3,101	83,472	11,047
Books 51–60	58,424	66,950	92,400	2,750	9,000	58,481	92,405	2,748	9,002	66,954
Books 61–70	7,682	5,313	83,000	87,000	89,170	7,675	83,021	87,008	89,167	5,311
Books 71–80	1,727	77,325	89,010	862	88,365	1,702	89,015	860	88,368	77,328
Books 81–90	46,926	84,799	88,045	927	89,790	46,986	88,042	926	89,766	84,796
Books 91–100	30,644	6,570	90,000	8,410	91,010	30,692	90,009	8,408	91,015	6,574
Books 101–110	35,968	44,763	89,210	510	9,247	35,940	89,213	512	9,249	44,766
Books 111–120	830	8,700	92,040	7,891	83,150	838	92,037	7,889	83,149	8,705
Books 121–130	702	92,410	94,505	38,860	81,110	712	94,503	87,797	81,111	92,412
Books 131–140	1,630	88,250	97,000	7,549	8,245	1,632	97,002	7,547	8,243	88,254
Books 141–150	47,180	75,000	89,241	81,234	8,735	47,192	89,239	81,238	8,739	75,010

Exercises 3–6

3. Follow your teacher's instructions to generate a set of 10 random numbers. Find the total number of words corresponding to each book identified by your random numbers.

4. Choose two more different random samples of size 10 from the data, and make a dot plot of each of the three samples.

5. If your teacher randomly chooses 10 books from your summer vacation reading list, would you be likely to get many books with a lot of words? Explain your thinking using statistical terms.

6. If you were to compare your samples to your classmates' samples, do you think your answer to Exercise 5 would change? Why or why not?

Exercises 7–9: A Statistical Study of Balance and Grade

7. Is the following question a statistical question: Do sixth graders or seventh graders tend to have better balance?

Lesson 16:   Methods for Selecting a Random Sample

EUREKA MATH

8. Berthio's class decided to measure balance by finding out how long people can stand on one foot.

a. How would you rephrase the question from Exercise 7 to create a statistical question using this definition of balance? Explain your reasoning.

b. What should the class think about to be consistent in how they collect the data if they actually have people stand on one foot and measure the time?

9. Work with your class to devise a plan to select a random sample of sixth graders and a random sample of seventh graders to measure their balance using Berthio's method. Then, write a paragraph describing how you will collect data to determine whether there is a difference in how long sixth graders and seventh graders can stand on one foot. Your plan should answer the following questions:

a. What is the population? How will samples be selected from the population? Why is it important that they be random samples?

b. How would you conduct the activity?

c. What sample statistics will you calculate, and how will you display and analyze the data?

d. What would you accept as evidence that there actually is a difference in how long sixth graders can stand on one foot compared to seventh graders?

Name _____ Date _____

1. Name two things to consider when you are planning how to select a random sample.

2. Consider a population consisting of the 200 seventh graders at a particular middle school. Describe how you might select a random sample of 20 students from a list of the students in this population.

> The population is all the teachers in my school.

1. The suggestions below describe ways to choose a random sample of teachers in your school that were made and vetoed. Explain why you think each was vetoed.

   a. Stand in the teachers' lounge, and use every teacher that enters before school.

   Teachers who do not enter the teachers' lounge in the morning do not have a chance to be selected, so the sample would not be random.

   > In order for a sample to be random, everyone in the population must have an equal chance of being selected.

   b. Use all the science teachers in the school.

   The teachers who do not teach science do not have a chance to be selected, so the sample would not be random.

2. The school wanted random seventh graders to complete a survey every week in order to gain information about students' thoughts about the school.

   a. Describe how the school might choose a random sample of 25 seventh graders from the total of 120 seventh graders in the school.

   Each seventh grade student could be assigned a number, and then the numbers could be placed in a bag. Every week, 25 numbers could be pulled from the bag to have students complete the survey.

   > I could also put all 120 names into a bag and pick 25 names every week.

   b. There are 40 weeks during the school year. If a random sample of 25 seventh graders is picked every week, would every student be chosen at least once? Why or why not?

   The probability of being chosen each week is $\frac{25}{120}$, or approximately 21%. Although the number of chances to get picked is high, the probability is low.

   > I could carry out the investigation to determine if it is likely for every student to be chosen.

1. The suggestions below for how to choose a random sample of students at your school were made and vetoed. Explain why you think each was vetoed.

   a. Use every fifth person you see in the hallway before class starts.

   b. Use all of the students taking math the same time that your class meets.

   c. Have students who come to school early do the activity before school starts.

   d. Have everyone in the class find two friends to be in the sample.

2. A teacher decided to collect homework from a random sample of her students rather than grading every paper every day.

   a. Describe how she might choose a random sample of five students from her class of 35 students.

   b. Suppose every day for 75 days throughout an entire semester she chooses a random sample of five students. Do you think some students will never get selected? Why or why not?

3. Think back to earlier lessons in which you chose a random sample. Describe how you could have used a random number generator to select a random sample in each case.

   a. A random sample of the words in the poem "Casey at the Bat"

   b. A random sample of the grocery prices on a weekly flyer

4. Sofia decided to use a different plan for selecting a random sample of books from the population of 150 top-selling children's books from Example 2. She generated ten random numbers between 1 and 100,000 to stand for the possible number of pages in any of the books. Then, she found the books that had the number of pages specified in the sample. What would you say to Sofia?

5. Find an example from a newspaper, a magazine, or another source that used a sample. Describe the population, the sample, the sample statistic, how you think the sample might have been chosen, and whether or not you think the sample was random.

Example 1: Estimating a Population Mean

The owners of a gym have been keeping track of how long each person spends at the gym. Eight hundred of these times (in minutes) are shown in the population tables located at the end of the lesson. These 800 times will form the *population* that you will investigate in this lesson.

Look at the values in the population. Can you find the longest time spent in the gym in the population? Can you find the shortest?

On average, roughly how long do you think people spend at the gym? In other words, by just looking at the numbers in the two tables, make an estimate of the *population mean*.

You could find the population mean by typing all 800 numbers into a calculator or a computer, adding them up, and dividing by 800. This would be extremely time consuming, and usually it is not possible to measure every value in a population.

Instead of doing a calculation using every value in the population, we will use a *random sample* to find the mean of the sample. The sample mean will then be used as an estimate of the population mean.

Example 2: Selecting a Sample Using a Table of Random Digits

The table of random digits provided with this lesson will be used to select items from a population to produce a random sample from the population. The list of digits is determined by a computer program that simulates a random selection of the digits 0, 1, 2, 3, 4, 5, 6, 7, 8, or 9. Imagine that each of these digits is written on a slip of paper and placed in a bag. After thoroughly mixing the bag, one slip is drawn, and its digit is recorded in this list of random digits. The slip is then returned to the bag, and another slip is selected. The digit on this slip is recorded and then returned to the bag. The process is repeated over and over. The resulting list of digits is called a *random number table*.

How could you use a table of random digits to take a random sample?

Step 1: Place the table of random digits in front of you. Without looking at the page, place the eraser end of your pencil somewhere on the table. Start using the table of random digits at the number closest to where your eraser touched the paper. This digit and the following two specify which observation from the population tables will be the first observation in your sample.

For example, suppose the eraser end of your pencil lands on the twelfth number in Row 3 of the random digit table. This number is 5, and the two following numbers are 1 and 4. This means that the first observation in your sample is observation number 514 from the population. Find observation number 514 in the population table. Do this by going to Row 51 and moving across to the column heading "4." This observation is 53, so the first observation in your sample is 53.

If the number from the random number table is any number 800 or greater, you will ignore this number and use the next three digits in the table.

Step 2: Continue using the table of random digits from the point you reached, and select the other four observations in your sample like you did in Step 1.

For example, continuing on from the position in the example given in Step 1:

- The next number from the random digit table is 716, and observation 716 is 63.
- The next number from the random digit table is 565, and observation 565 is 31.
- The next number from the random digit table is 911, and there is no observation 911. So, we ignore these three digits.
- The next number from the random digit table is 928, and there is no observation 928. So, we ignore these three digits.
- The next number from the random digit table is 303, and observation 303 is 70.
- The next number from the random digit table is 677, and observation 677 is 42.

Exercises 1–4

Initially, you will select just five values from the population to form your sample. This is a very small sample size, but it is a good place to start to understand the ideas of this lesson.

1. Use the table of random numbers to select five values from the population of times. What are the five observations in your sample?

2. For the sample that you selected, calculate the sample mean.

3. You selected a random sample and calculated the sample mean in order to estimate the population mean. Do you think that the mean of these five observations is exactly correct for the population mean? Could the population mean be greater than the number you calculated? Could the population mean be less than the number you calculated?

Lesson 17:   Sampling Variability

4. In practice, you only take one sample in order to estimate a population characteristic. But, for the purposes of this lesson, suppose you were to take another random sample from the same population of times at the gym. Could the new sample mean be closer to the population mean than the mean of these five observations? Could it be farther from the population mean?

Exercises 5–7

As a class, you will now investigate sampling variability by taking several samples from the same population. Each sample will have a different sample mean. This variation provides an example of sampling variability.

5. Place the table of random digits in front of you, and without looking at the page, place the eraser end of your pencil somewhere on the table of random numbers. Start using the table of random digits at the number closest to where your eraser touches the paper. This digit and the following two specify which observation from the population tables will be the first observation in your sample. Write this three-digit number and the corresponding data value from the population in the space below.

6. Continue moving to the right in the table of random digits from the place you ended in Exercise 5. Use three digits at a time. Each set of three digits specifies which observation in the population is the next number in your sample. Continue until you have four more observations, and write these four values in the space below.

7. Calculate the mean of the five values that form your sample. Round your answer to the nearest tenth. Show your work and your sample mean in the space below.

Exercises 8–11

You will now use the sample means from Exercise 7 from the entire class to make a dot plot.

8. Write the sample means for everyone in the class in the space below.

9. Use all the sample means to make a dot plot using the axis given below. (Remember, if you have repeated or close values, stack the dots one above the other.)

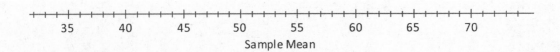

Sample Mean

10. What do you see in the dot plot that demonstrates sampling variability?

11. Remember that in practice you only take one sample. (In this lesson, many samples were taken in order to demonstrate the concept of sampling variability.) Suppose that a statistician plans to take a random sample of size 5 from the population of times spent at the gym and that he will use the sample mean as an estimate of the population mean. Approximately how far can the statistician expect the sample mean to be from the population mean?

EUREKA
MATH®

Lesson Summary

A population characteristic is estimated by taking a random sample from the population and calculating the value of a statistic for the sample. For example, a population mean is estimated by selecting a random sample from the population and calculating the sample mean.

The value of the sample statistic (e.g., the sample mean) will vary based on the random sample that is selected. This variation from sample to sample in the values of the sample statistic is called *sampling variability*.

Population

	0	1	2	3	4	5	6	7	8	9
00	45	58	49	78	59	36	52	39	70	51
01	50	45	45	66	71	55	65	33	60	51
02	53	83	40	51	83	57	75	38	43	77
03	49	49	81	57	42	36	22	66	68	52
04	60	67	43	60	55	63	56	44	50	58
05	64	41	67	73	55	69	63	46	50	65
06	54	58	53	55	51	74	53	55	64	16
07	28	48	62	24	82	51	64	45	41	47
08	70	50	38	16	39	83	62	50	37	58
09	79	62	45	48	42	51	67	68	56	78
10	61	56	71	55	57	77	48	65	61	62
11	65	40	56	47	44	51	38	68	64	40
12	53	22	73	62	82	78	84	50	43	43
13	81	42	72	49	55	65	41	92	50	60
14	56	44	40	70	52	47	30	9	58	53
15	84	64	64	34	37	69	57	75	62	67
16	45	58	49	78	59	36	52	39	70	51
17	50	45	45	66	71	55	65	33	60	51
18	53	83	40	51	83	57	75	38	43	77
19	49	49	81	57	42	36	22	66	68	52
20	60	67	43	60	55	63	56	44	50	58
21	64	41	67	73	55	69	63	46	50	65
22	54	58	53	55	51	74	53	55	64	16
23	28	48	62	24	82	51	64	45	41	47
24	70	50	38	16	39	83	62	50	37	58
25	79	62	45	48	42	51	67	68	56	78
26	61	56	71	55	57	77	48	65	61	62
27	65	40	56	47	44	51	38	68	64	40
28	53	22	73	62	82	78	84	50	43	43
29	81	42	72	49	55	65	41	92	50	60
30	56	44	40	70	52	47	30	9	58	53
31	84	64	64	34	37	69	57	75	62	67
32	45	58	49	78	59	36	52	39	70	51
33	50	45	45	66	71	55	65	33	60	51
34	53	83	40	51	83	57	75	38	43	77
35	49	49	81	57	42	36	22	66	68	52
36	60	67	43	60	55	63	56	44	50	58
37	64	41	67	73	55	69	63	46	50	65
38	54	58	53	55	51	74	53	55	64	16
39	28	48	62	24	82	51	64	45	41	47

Lesson 17:   Sampling Variability

Population (continued)

	0	1	2	3	4	5	6	7	8	9
40	53	70	59	62	33	31	74	44	46	68
41	37	51	84	47	46	33	53	54	70	74
42	35	45	48	45	56	60	66	60	65	57
43	42	81	67	64	60	79	46	48	67	56
44	41	21	41	58	48	38	50	53	73	38
45	35	28	43	43	55	39	75	45	68	36
46	64	31	31	40	84	79	47	63	48	46
47	34	36	54	61	33	16	50	60	52	55
48	53	52	48	47	77	37	66	51	61	64
49	40	44	45	22	36	64	50	49	64	39
50	45	69	67	33	55	61	62	38	51	43
51	55	39	46	56	53	50	44	42	40	60
52	11	36	56	69	72	73	71	48	58	52
53	81	47	36	54	81	59	50	42	80	69
54	40	43	30	54	61	13	73	65	52	40
55	71	78	71	61	54	79	63	47	49	73
56	53	70	59	62	33	31	74	44	46	68
57	37	51	84	47	46	33	53	54	70	74
58	35	45	48	45	56	60	66	60	65	57
59	42	81	67	64	60	79	46	48	67	56
60	41	21	41	58	48	38	50	53	73	38
61	35	28	43	43	55	39	75	45	68	36
62	64	31	31	40	84	79	47	63	48	46
63	34	36	54	61	33	16	50	60	52	55
64	53	52	48	47	77	37	66	51	61	64
65	40	44	45	22	36	64	50	49	64	39
66	45	69	67	33	55	61	62	38	51	43
67	55	39	46	56	53	50	44	42	40	60
68	11	36	56	69	72	73	71	48	58	52
69	81	47	36	54	81	59	50	42	80	69
70	40	43	30	54	61	13	73	65	52	40
71	71	78	71	61	54	79	63	47	49	73
72	53	70	59	62	33	31	74	44	46	68
73	37	51	84	47	46	33	53	54	70	74
74	35	45	48	45	56	60	66	60	65	57
75	42	81	67	64	60	79	46	48	67	56
76	41	21	41	58	48	38	50	53	73	38
77	35	28	43	43	55	39	75	45	68	36
78	64	31	31	40	84	79	47	63	48	46
79	34	36	54	61	33	16	50	60	52	55

EUREKA
MATH

Table of Random Digits

Row																				
1	6	6	7	2	8	0	0	8	4	0	0	4	6	0	3	2	2	4	6	8
2	8	0	3	1	1	1	1	2	7	0	1	9	1	2	7	1	3	3	5	3
3	5	3	5	7	3	6	3	1	7	2	5	5	1	4	7	1	6	5	6	5
4	9	1	1	9	2	8	3	0	3	6	7	7	4	7	5	9	8	1	8	3
5	9	0	2	9	9	7	4	6	3	6	6	3	7	4	2	7	0	0	1	9
6	8	1	4	6	4	6	8	2	8	9	5	5	2	9	6	2	5	3	0	3
7	4	1	1	9	7	0	7	2	9	0	9	7	0	4	6	2	3	1	0	9
8	9	9	2	7	1	3	2	9	0	3	9	0	7	5	6	7	1	7	8	7
9	3	4	2	2	9	1	9	0	7	8	1	6	2	5	3	9	0	9	1	0
10	2	7	3	9	5	9	9	3	2	9	3	9	1	9	0	5	5	1	4	2
11	0	2	5	4	0	8	1	7	0	7	1	3	0	4	3	0	6	4	4	4
12	8	6	0	5	4	8	8	2	7	7	0	1	0	1	7	1	3	5	3	4
13	4	2	6	4	5	2	4	2	6	1	7	5	6	6	4	0	8	4	1	2
14	4	4	9	8	7	3	4	3	8	2	9	1	5	3	5	9	8	9	2	9
15	6	4	8	0	0	0	4	2	3	8	1	8	4	0	9	5	0	9	0	4
16	3	2	3	8	4	8	8	6	2	9	1	0	1	9	9	3	0	7	3	5
17	6	6	7	2	8	0	0	8	4	0	0	4	6	0	3	2	2	4	6	8
18	8	0	3	1	1	1	1	2	7	0	1	9	1	2	7	1	3	3	5	3
19	5	3	5	7	3	6	3	1	7	2	5	5	1	4	7	1	6	5	6	5
20	9	1	1	9	2	8	3	0	3	6	7	7	4	7	5	9	8	1	8	3
21	9	0	2	9	9	7	4	6	3	6	6	3	7	4	2	7	0	0	1	9
22	8	1	4	6	4	6	8	2	8	9	5	5	2	9	6	2	5	3	0	3
23	4	1	1	9	7	0	7	2	9	0	9	7	0	4	6	2	3	1	0	9
24	9	9	2	7	1	3	2	9	0	3	9	0	7	5	6	7	1	7	8	7
25	3	4	2	2	9	1	9	0	7	8	1	6	2	5	3	9	0	9	1	0
26	2	7	3	9	5	9	9	3	2	9	3	9	1	9	0	5	5	1	4	2
27	0	2	5	4	0	8	1	7	0	7	1	3	0	4	3	0	6	4	4	4
28	8	6	0	5	4	8	8	2	7	7	0	1	0	1	7	1	3	5	3	4
29	4	2	6	4	5	2	4	2	6	1	7	5	6	6	4	0	8	4	1	2
30	4	4	9	8	7	3	4	3	8	2	9	1	5	3	5	9	8	9	2	9
31	6	4	8	0	0	0	4	2	3	8	1	8	4	0	9	5	0	9	0	4
32	3	2	3	8	4	8	8	6	2	9	1	0	1	9	9	3	0	7	3	5
33	6	6	7	2	8	0	0	8	4	0	0	4	6	0	3	2	2	4	6	8
34	8	0	3	1	1	1	1	2	7	0	1	9	1	2	7	1	3	3	5	3
35	5	3	5	7	3	6	3	1	7	2	5	5	1	4	7	1	6	5	6	5
36	9	1	1	9	2	8	3	0	3	6	7	7	4	7	5	9	8	1	8	3
37	9	0	2	9	9	7	4	6	3	6	6	3	7	4	2	7	0	0	1	9
38	8	1	4	6	4	6	8	2	8	9	5	5	2	9	6	2	5	3	0	3
39	4	1	1	9	7	0	7	2	9	0	9	7	0	4	6	2	3	1	0	9
40	9	9	2	7	1	3	2	9	0	3	9	0	7	5	6	7	1	7	8	7

Name _____   Date _____

Suppose that you want to estimate the mean time per evening students at your school spend doing homework. You will do this using a random sample of 30 students.

1. Suppose that you have a list of all the students at your school. The students are numbered 1, 2, 3,.... One way to select the random sample of students is to use the random digit table from today's class, taking three digits at a time. If you start at the third digit of Row 9, what is the number of the first student you would include in your sample?

2. Suppose that you have now selected your random sample and that you have asked the students how long they spend doing homework each evening. How will you use these results to estimate the mean time spent doing homework for *all* students?

3. Explain what is meant by *sampling variability* in this context.

1. Holly is trying to convince her mom that she needs a fancy dress for prom. She wants to estimate the mean price girls at her school pay (in dollars) for prom dresses at this time. Holly selects a random sample of 12 girls from her school and asks what they paid for their prom dress. The results are shown below.

100   54   32   97   68   89   142   61   77   106   96   49

a. Holly will estimate the mean dress cost of all dresses bought by girls at her school by calculating the mean for her sample. Calculate the sample mean, and record your answer below.

$$\frac{100 + 54 + 32 + 97 + 68 + 89 + 142 + 61 + 77 + 106 + 96 + 49}{12} = \frac{971}{12} \approx 80.9$$

> To calculate the mean, I add all the data values together and then divide by the number of data values, 12.

The mean cost of a prom dress is approximately $81.00.

b. If Holly collected another sample of dress prices, would the result be the same?

It is not likely that another sample would have the same mean as this one.

> It is very rare that two samples will result in the exact same mean.

c. Explain why the means of a variety of samples will be different.

Sample variability explains that there will be differences between samples of the same population, which would result in different means.

2. Think about the mean number of pets for all students at your school.

a. What do you think is the approximate value of the mean number of pets for the population of students at your school?

The mean number of pets is 2.

> Answers will vary but should be realistic.

b. How could you find a better estimate of this population mean?

I could ask a random sample of students how many pets they have and then calculate the sample mean.

I calculate the mean by calculating the sum of all the data values and dividing by the number of data values. Due to sampling variability, I know each sample could have a different mean.

Lesson 17:   Sampling Variability

1. Yousef intends to buy a car. He wishes to estimate the mean fuel efficiency (in miles per gallon) of all cars available at this time. Yousef selects a random sample of 10 cars and looks up their fuel efficiencies on the Internet. The results are shown below.

    22 25 29 23 31 29 28 22 23 27

    a. Yousef will estimate the mean fuel efficiency of all cars by calculating the mean for his sample. Calculate the sample mean, and record your answer. (Be sure to show your work.)

    b. In practice, you only take one sample to estimate a population characteristic. However, if Yousef were to take another random sample of 10 cars from the same population, would he likely get the same value for the sample mean?

    c. What if Yousef were to take *many* random samples of 10 cars? Would all of the sample means be the same?

    d. Using this example, explain what sampling variability means.

2. Think about the mean number of siblings (brothers and sisters) for all students at your school.

    a. What do you think is the approximate value of the mean number of siblings for the population of all students at your school?

    b. How could you find a better estimate of this population mean?

    c. Suppose that you have now selected a random sample of students from your school. You have asked all of the students in your sample how many siblings they have. How will you calculate the sample mean?

    d. If you had taken a different sample, would the sample mean have taken the same value?

    e. There are many different samples of students that you could have selected. These samples produce many different possible sample means. What is the phrase used for this concept?

    f. Does the phrase you gave in part (e) apply only to sample means?

Example 1: Sampling Variability

The previous lesson investigated the statistical question "What is the typical time spent at the gym?" by selecting random samples from the population of 800 gym members. Two different dot plots of sample means calculated from random samples from the population are displayed below. The first dot plot represents the means of 20 samples with each sample having 5 data points. The second dot plot represents the means of 20 samples with each sample having 15 data points.

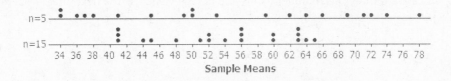

Based on the first dot plot, Jill answered the statistical question by indicating the mean time people spent at the gym was between 34 and 78 minutes. She decided that a time approximately in the middle of that interval would be her estimate of the mean time the 800 people spent at the gym. She estimated 52 minutes. Scott answered the question using the second dot plot. He indicated that the mean time people spent at the gym was between 41 and 65 minutes. He also selected a time of 52 minutes to answer the question.

    a.   Describe the differences in the two dot plots.

    b.   Which dot plot do you feel more confident in using to answer the statistical question? Explain your answer.

    c.   In general, do you want sampling variability to be large or small? Explain.

Exercises 1–3

In the previous lesson, you saw a population of 800 times spent at the gym. You will now select a random sample of size 15 from that population. You will then calculate the sample mean.

1. Start by selecting a three-digit number from the table of random digits. Place the random digit table in front of you. Without looking at the page, place the eraser end of your pencil somewhere on the table of random digits. Start using the table of random digits at the digit closest to your eraser. This digit and the following two specify which observation from the population will be the first observation in your sample. Write the value of this observation in the space below. (Discard any three-digit number that is 800 or larger, and use the next three digits from the random digit table.)

2. Continue moving to the right in the table of random digits from the point that you reached in Exercise 1. Each three-digit number specifies a value to be selected from the population. Continue in this way until you have selected 14 more values from the population. This will make 15 values altogether. Write the values of all 15 observations in the space below.

3. Calculate the mean of your 15 sample values. Write the value of your sample mean below. Round your answer to the nearest tenth. (Be sure to show your work.)

Exercises 4–6

You will now use the sample means from Exercise 3 for the entire class to make a dot plot.

4. Write the sample means for everyone in the class in the space below.

Lesson 18:   Sampling Variability and the Effect of Sample Size

5. Use all the sample means to make a dot plot using the axis given below. (Remember, if you have repeated values or values close to each other, stack the dots one above the other.)

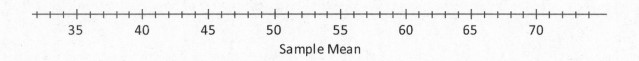

6. In the previous lesson, you drew a dot plot of sample means for samples of size 5. How does the dot plot above (of sample means for samples of size 15) compare to the dot plot of sample means for samples of size 5? For which sample size (5 or 15) does the sample mean have the greater sampling variability?

    This exercise illustrates the notion that the greater the sample size, the smaller the sampling variability of the sample mean.

Exercises 7–8

7. Remember that in practice you only take one sample. Suppose that a statistician plans to take a random sample of size 15 from the population of times spent at the gym and will use the sample mean as an estimate of the population mean. Based on the dot plot of sample means that your class collected from the population, approximately how far can the statistician expect the sample mean to be from the population mean? (The actual population mean is 53.9 minutes.)

8. How would your answer in Exercise 7 compare to the equivalent mean of the distances for a sample of size 5?

Exercises 9–11

Suppose everyone in your class selected a random sample of size 25 from the population of times spent at the gym.

9.   What do you think the dot plot of the class's sample means would look like? Make a sketch using the axis below.

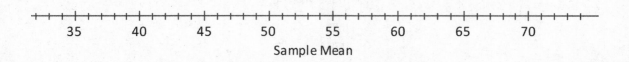

Sample Mean

10. Suppose that a statistician plans to estimate the population mean using a sample of size 25. According to your sketch, approximately how far can the statistician expect the sample mean to be from the population mean?

11. Suppose you have a choice of using a sample of size 5, 15, or 25. Which of the three makes the sampling variability of the sample mean the smallest? Why would you choose the sample size that makes the sampling variability of the sample mean as small as possible?

Name _____ Date _____

Suppose that you wanted to estimate the mean time per evening spent doing homework for students at your school. You decide to do this by taking a random sample of students from your school. You will calculate the mean time spent doing homework for your sample. You will then use your sample mean as an estimate of the population mean.

1. The sample mean has *sampling variability*. Explain what this means.

2. When you are using a sample statistic to estimate a population characteristic, do you want the sampling variability of the sample statistic to be large or small? Explain why.

3. Think about your estimate of the mean time spent doing homework for students at your school. Given a choice of using a sample of size 20 or a sample of size 40, which should you choose? Explain your answer.

The distances, in miles, that 200 people have to travel to the airport are recorded in the table below.

	0	1	2	3	4	5	6	7	8	9
00	45	58	49	78	59	36	52	39	70	51
01	50	45	45	66	71	55	65	33	60	51
02	53	83	40	51	83	57	75	38	43	77
03	49	49	81	57	42	36	22	66	68	52
04	60	67	43	60	55	63	56	44	50	58
05	64	41	67	73	55	69	63	46	50	65
06	54	58	53	55	51	74	53	55	64	16
07	28	48	62	24	82	51	64	45	41	47
08	70	50	38	16	39	83	62	50	37	58
09	79	62	45	48	42	51	67	68	56	78
10	61	56	71	55	57	77	48	65	61	62
11	65	40	56	47	44	51	38	68	64	40
12	53	22	73	62	82	78	84	50	43	43
13	81	42	72	49	55	65	41	92	50	60
14	56	44	40	70	52	47	30	9	58	53
15	84	64	64	34	37	69	57	75	62	67
16	45	58	49	78	59	36	52	39	70	51
17	50	45	45	66	71	55	65	33	60	51
18	53	83	40	51	83	57	75	38	43	77
19	49	49	81	57	42	36	22	66	68	52

1. Using the random digit table, the following 15 values were chosen.

    82, 64, 40, 64, 33, 81, 22, 50, 66, 51, 78, 49, 70, 58, 84

> I add the data values together and divide by the number of data values.

Calculate the mean of the sample.

$$\frac{82 + 64 + 40 + 64 + 33 + 81 + 22 + 50 + 66 + 51 + 78 + 49 + 70 + 58 + 84}{15} = \frac{892}{15} \approx 59.5$$

The average distance people travel to the airport is approximately 59.5 miles.

2. Using the random digit table, the following 25 values were chosen.

    45, 67, 71, 49, 50, 38, 67, 77, 55, 45, 64, 22, 36, 9, 49, 30, 51, 70, 75, 36, 73, 62, 79, 50, 40

    Calculate the mean of the sample.

    $$\frac{1310}{25} = 52.4$$

    The average distance people travel to the airport is 52.4 miles.

3. Which sample mean would you expect to be closer to the population mean? Explain your reasoning.

    The sample mean from Problem 2 would be closer the population mean because the sample size is greater.

    > The sample variability is smaller with a larger sample and larger with a smaller sample.

Lesson 18:   Sampling Variability and the Effect of Sample Size

EUREKA MATH

1. The owner of a new coffee shop is keeping track of how much each customer spends (in dollars). One hundred of these amounts are shown in the table below. These amounts will form the *population* for this question.

	0	1	2	3	4	5	6	7	8	9
0	6.18	4.67	4.01	4.06	3.28	4.47	4.86	4.91	3.96	6.18
1	4.98	5.42	5.65	2.97	2.92	7.09	2.78	4.20	5.02	4.98
2	3.12	1.89	4.19	5.12	4.38	5.34	4.22	4.27	5.25	3.12
3	3.90	4.47	4.07	4.80	6.28	5.79	6.07	7.64	6.33	3.90
4	5.55	4.99	3.77	3.63	5.21	3.85	7.43	4.72	6.53	5.55
5	4.55	5.38	5.83	4.10	4.42	5.63	5.57	5.32	5.32	4.55
6	4.56	7.67	6.39	4.05	4.51	5.16	5.29	6.34	3.68	4.56
7	5.86	4.75	4.94	3.92	4.84	4.95	4.50	4.56	7.05	5.86
8	5.00	5.47	5.00	5.70	5.71	6.19	4.41	4.29	4.34	5.00
9	5.12	5.58	6.16	6.39	5.93	3.72	5.92	4.82	6.19	5.12

a. Place the table of random digits in front of you. Select a starting point without looking at the page. Then, taking two digits at a time, select a random sample of size 10 from the population above. Write the 10 values in the space below. (For example, suppose you start at the third digit of row four of the random digit table. Taking two digits gives you 19. In the population above, go to the row labeled 1, and move across to the column labeled 9. This observation is 4.98, and that will be the first observation in your sample. Then, continue in the random digit table from the point you reached.)

   Calculate the mean for your sample, showing your work. Round your answer to the nearest thousandth.

b. Using the same approach as in part (a), select a random sample of size 20 from the population.
   Calculate the mean for your sample of size 20. Round your answer to the nearest thousandth.

c. Which of your sample means is likely to be the better estimate of the population mean? Explain your answer in terms of sampling variability.

2. Two dot plots are shown below. One of the dot plots shows the values of some sample means from random samples of size 10 from the population given in Problem 1. The other dot plot shows the values of some sample means from random samples of size 20 from the population given in Problem 1.

Dot Plot A

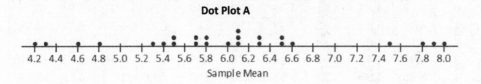

Sample Mean

Dot Plot B

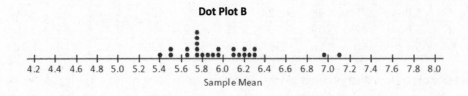

Sample Mean

Which dot plot is for sample means from samples of size 10, and which dot plot is for sample means from samples of size 20? Explain your reasoning.

The sample means from samples of size 10 are shown in Dot Plot _____.

The sample means from samples of size 20 are shown in Dot Plot _____.

3. You are going to use a random sample to estimate the mean travel time for getting to school for all the students in your grade. You will select a random sample of students from your grade. Explain why you would like the sampling variability of the sample mean to be *small*.

EUREKA MATH

In a previous lesson, you selected several random samples from a population. You recorded values of a numerical variable. You then calculated the mean for each sample, saw that there was variability in the sample means, and created a distribution of sample means to better see the sampling variability. You then considered larger samples and saw that the variability in the distribution decreases when the sample size increases. In this lesson, you will use a similar process to investigate variability in sample proportions.

Example 1: Sample Proportion

Your teacher will give your group a bag that contains colored cubes, some of which are red. With your classmates, you are going to build a distribution of sample proportions.

a. Each person in your group should randomly select a sample of 10 cubes from the bag. Record the data for your sample in the table below.

Cube	Outcome (Color)
1	
2	
3	
4	
5	
6	
7	
8	
9	
10	

b. What is the proportion of red cubes in your sample of 10?

This value is called the *sample proportion*. The sample proportion is found by dividing the number of successes (in this example, the number of red cubes) by the total number of observations in the sample.

c. Write your sample proportion on a sticky note, and place it on the number line that your teacher has drawn on the board. Place your note above the value on the number line that corresponds to your sample proportion. The graph of all students' sample proportions is called a *sampling distribution* of the sample proportions.

d. Describe the shape of the distribution.

e. Describe the variability in the sample proportions.

Based on the distribution, answer the following:

f. What do you think is the population proportion?

g. How confident are you of your estimate?

Lesson 19:   Understanding Variability When Estimating
                       a Population Proportion

EUREKA MATH

Example 2: Sampling Variability

What do you think would happen to the sampling distribution if everyone in class took a random sample of 30 cubes from the bag? To help answer this question, you will repeat the random sampling you did in part (a) of Example 1, except now you will draw a random sample of 30 cubes instead of 10.

a. Take a random sample of 30 cubes from the bag. Carefully record the outcome of each draw.

Cube	Outcome (Color)	Cube	Outcome (Color)
1		16	
2		17	
3		18	
4		19	
5		20	
6		21	
7		22	
8		23	
9		24	
10		25	
11		26	
12		27	
13		28	
14		29	
15		30	

b. What is the proportion of red cubes in your sample of 30?

c. Write your sample proportion on a sticky note, and place the note on the number line that your teacher has drawn on the board. Place your note above the value on the number line that corresponds to your sample proportion.

d. Describe the shape of the distribution.

Exercises 1–5

1. Describe the variability in the sample proportions.

2. Based on the distribution, answer the following:

   a. What do you think is the population proportion?

   b. How confident are you of your estimate?

   c. If you were taking a random sample of 30 cubes and determined the proportion that was red, do you think your sample proportion will be within 0.05 of the population proportion? Explain.

3. Compare the sampling distribution based on samples of size 10 to the sampling distribution based on samples of size 30.

4. As the sample size increased from 10 to 30, describe what happened to the sampling variability of the sample proportions.

5. What do you think would happen to the sampling variability of the sample proportions if the sample size for each sample was 50 instead of 30? Explain.

    Lesson 19:   Understanding Variability When Estimating
                  a Population Proportion

EUREKA MATH

Lesson Summary

- The sampling distribution of the sample proportion is a graph of the sample proportions for many different samples.

- The mean of the sample proportions will be approximately equal to the value of the population proportion.

- As the sample size increases, the sampling variability decreases.

Name _____   Date _____

A group of seventh graders took repeated samples of size 20 from a bag of colored cubes. The dot plot below shows the sampling distribution of the sample proportion of blue cubes in the bag.

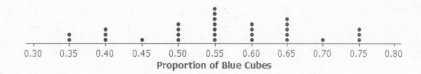

1. Describe the shape of the distribution.

2. Describe the variability of the distribution.

3. Predict how the dot plot would look differently if the sample sizes had been 40 instead of 20.

A group of friends want to determine the number of chocolate pieces of candy in a bag of mixed candy. Each friend took a random sample of 10 pieces of candy. The table below shows the proportion of chocolate pieces of candy each friend found.

0.2	0.7	0.5	0.7	0.6
0.5	0.4	0.7	0.6	0.5
0.2	0.8	0.6	0.6	0.5

1. Construct a dot plot of the sample proportions.

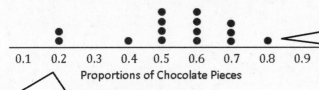

Dot Plot of Proportions of Chocolate Pieces

Proportions of Chocolate Pieces

Each dot represents one data value. If a value is represented more than once in the distribution, I place the additional dots above the original dot.

The number line of a dot plot must have a constant scale. I cannot skip numbers, even if a number is not represented in the distribution.

2. Describe the variability of the distribution.

   The spread of the data is 0.2 to 0.8; however, most of the data is between 0.5 and 0.7.

   I know the sampling variability decreases when my sample size increases.

   The spread explains the location of the data values using the minimum and maximum.

3. Suppose each friend picked 40 pieces of candy from the bag. Describe how the sampling distribution would change from the one you constructed in Problem 1.

   The sampling variability would decrease.

1. A class of seventh graders wanted to find the proportion of M&M's® that are red. Each seventh grader took a random sample of 20 M&M's® from a very large container of M&M's®. The following is the proportion of red M&M's each student found.

0.15	0	0.1	0.1	0.05	0.1	0.2	0.05	0.1
0.1	0.15	0.2	0	0.1	0.15	0.15	0.1	0.2
0.3	0.1	0.1	0.2	0.1	0.15	0.1	0.05	0.3

a. Construct a dot plot of the sample proportions.

b. Describe the shape of the distribution.

c. Describe the variability of the distribution.

d. Suppose the seventh-grade students had taken random samples of size 50. Describe how the sampling distribution would change from the one you constructed in part (a).

2. A group of seventh graders wanted to estimate the proportion of middle school students who suffer from allergies. The members of one group of seventh graders each took a random sample of 10 middle school students, and the members of another group of seventh graders each took a random sample of 40 middle school students. Below are two sampling distributions of the sample proportions of middle school students who said that they suffer from allergies. Which dot plot is based on random samples of size 40? How can you tell?

Dot Plot A:

Dot Plot of Sample Proportion

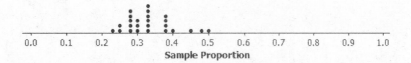

Dot Plot B:

Dot Plot of Sample Proportion

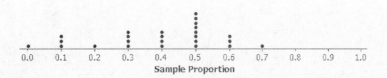

3. The nurse in your school district would like to study the proportion of middle school students who usually get at least eight hours of sleep on school nights. Suppose each student in your class plans on taking a random sample of 20 middle school students from your district, and each calculates a sample proportion of students who said that they usually get at least eight hours of sleep on school nights.

a. Do you expect everyone in your class to get the same value for their sample proportions? Explain.

b. Suppose each student in class increased the sample size from 20 to 40. Describe how you could reduce the sampling variability.

Lesson 19:   Understanding Variability When Estimating
               a Population Proportion

EUREKA
MATH

In a previous lesson, each student in your class selected a random sample from a population and calculated the sample proportion. It was observed that there was sampling variability in the sample proportions, and as the sample size increased, the variability decreased. In this lesson, you will investigate how sample proportions can be used to estimate population proportions.

Example 1: Mean of Sample Proportions

A class of 30 seventh graders wanted to estimate the proportion of middle school students who were vegetarians. Each seventh grader took a random sample of 20 middle school students. Students were asked the question, "Are you a vegetarian?" One sample of 20 students had three students who said that they were vegetarians. For this sample, the sample proportion is $\frac{3}{20}$, or 0.15. The following are the proportions of vegetarians the seventh graders found in 30 samples. Each sample was of size 20 students. The proportions are rounded to the nearest hundredth.

0.15	0.10	0.15	0.00	0.10	0.15	0.10	0.10	0.05	0.20
0.25	0.15	0.25	0.25	0.30	0.20	0.10	0.20	0.05	0.10
0.10	0.30	0.15	0.05	0.25	0.15	0.20	0.10	0.20	0.15

Exercises 1–9

1. The first student reported a sample proportion of 0.15. Interpret this value in terms of the summary of the problem in the example.

2. Another student reported a sample proportion of 0. Did this student do something wrong when selecting the sample of middle school students?

3. Assume you were part of this seventh-grade class and you got a sample proportion of 0.20 from a random sample of middle school students. Based on this sample proportion, what is your estimate for the proportion of all middle school students who are vegetarians?

4. Construct a dot plot of the 30 sample proportions.

5. Describe the shape of the distribution.

6. Using the 30 class results listed on the previous page, what is your estimate for the proportion of all middle school students who are vegetarians? Explain how you made this estimate.

7. Calculate the mean of the 30 sample proportions. How close is this value to the estimate you made in Exercise 6?

EUREKA
MATH®

8. The proportion of all middle school students who are vegetarians is 0.15. This is the actual proportion for the entire population of middle school students used to select the samples. How the mean of the 30 sample proportions compares with the actual population proportion depends on the students' samples.

9. Do the sample proportions in the dot plot tend to cluster around the value of the population proportion? Are any of the sample proportions far away from 0.15? List the proportions that are far away from 0.15.

Example 2: Estimating Population Proportion

Two hundred middle school students at Roosevelt Middle School responded to several survey questions. A printed copy of the responses the students gave to various questions will be provided by your teacher.

The data are organized in columns and are summarized by the following table:

Column Heading	Description
ID	Numbers from 1 to 200
Travel to School	Method used to get to school: Walk, car, rail, bus, bicycle, skateboard/scooter/rollerblade, boat
Favorite Season	Summer, fall, winter, spring
Allergies	Yes or no
Favorite School Subject	Art, English, languages, social studies, history, geography, music, science, computers, math, PE, other
Favorite Music	Classical, country, heavy metal, jazz, pop, punk rock, rap, reggae, R&B, rock and roll, techno, gospel, other
What superpower would you like?	Invisibility, super strength, telepathy, fly, freeze time

The last column in the data file is based on the question: Which of the following superpowers would you most like to have? The choices were invisibility, super strength, telepathy, fly, or freeze time.

The class wants to determine the proportion of Roosevelt Middle School students who answered "freeze time" to the last question. You will use a sample of the Roosevelt Middle School population to estimate the proportion of the students who answered "freeze time" to the last question.

A random sample of 20 student responses is needed. You are provided the random number table you used in a previous lesson. A printed list of the 200 Roosevelt Middle School students is also provided. In small groups, complete the following exercise:

a. Select a random sample of 20 student responses from the data file. Explain how you selected the random sample.

b. In the table below, list the 20 responses for your sample.

	Response
1	
2	
3	
4	
5	
6	
7	
8	
9	
10	
11	
12	
13	
14	
15	
16	
17	
18	
19	
20	

c. Estimate the population proportion of students who responded "freeze time" by calculating the sample proportion of the 20 sampled students who responded "freeze time" to the question.

Lesson 20:   Estimating a Population Proportion

EUREKA MATH

d. Combine your sample proportion with other students' sample proportions, and create a dot plot of the distribution of the sample proportions of students who responded "freeze time" to the question.

e. By looking at the dot plot, what is the value of the proportion of the 200 Roosevelt Middle School students who responded "freeze time" to the question?

f. Usually, you will estimate the proportion of Roosevelt Middle School students using just a single sample proportion. How different was your sample proportion from your estimate based on the dot plot of many samples?

g. Circle your sample proportion on the dot plot. How does your sample proportion compare with the mean of all the sample proportions?

h. Calculate the mean of all of the sample proportions. Locate the mean of the sample proportions in your dot plot; mark this position with an X. How does the mean of the sample proportions compare with your sample proportion?

Table of Random Digits

Row																				
1	6	6	7	2	8	0	0	8	4	0	0	4	6	0	3	2	2	4	6	8
2	8	0	3	1	1	1	1	2	7	0	1	9	1	2	7	1	3	3	5	3
3	5	3	5	7	3	6	3	1	7	2	5	5	1	4	7	1	6	5	6	5
4	9	1	1	9	2	8	3	0	3	6	7	7	4	7	5	9	8	1	8	3
5	9	0	2	9	9	7	4	6	3	6	6	3	7	4	2	7	0	0	1	9
6	8	1	4	6	4	6	8	2	8	9	5	5	2	9	6	2	5	3	0	3
7	4	1	1	9	7	0	7	2	9	0	9	7	0	4	6	2	3	1	0	9
8	9	9	2	7	1	3	2	9	0	3	9	0	7	5	6	7	1	7	8	7
9	3	4	2	2	9	1	9	0	7	8	1	6	2	5	3	9	0	9	1	0
10	2	7	3	9	5	9	9	3	2	9	3	9	1	9	0	5	5	1	4	2
11	0	2	5	4	0	8	1	7	0	7	1	3	0	4	3	0	6	4	4	4
12	8	6	0	5	4	8	8	2	7	7	0	1	0	1	7	1	3	5	3	4
13	4	2	6	4	5	2	4	2	6	1	7	5	6	6	4	0	8	4	1	2
14	4	4	9	8	7	3	4	3	8	2	9	1	5	3	5	9	8	9	2	9
15	6	4	8	0	0	0	4	2	3	8	1	8	4	0	9	5	0	9	0	4
16	3	2	3	8	4	8	8	6	2	9	1	0	1	9	9	3	0	7	3	5
17	6	6	7	2	8	0	0	8	4	0	0	4	6	0	3	2	2	4	6	8
18	8	0	3	1	1	1	1	2	7	0	1	9	1	2	7	1	3	3	5	3
19	5	3	5	7	3	6	3	1	7	2	5	5	1	4	7	1	6	5	6	5
20	9	1	1	9	2	8	3	0	3	6	7	7	4	7	5	9	8	1	8	3
21	9	0	2	9	9	7	4	6	3	6	6	3	7	4	2	7	0	0	1	9
22	8	1	4	6	4	6	8	2	8	9	5	5	2	9	6	2	5	3	0	3
23	4	1	1	9	7	0	7	2	9	0	9	7	0	4	6	2	3	1	0	9
24	9	9	2	7	1	3	2	9	0	3	9	0	7	5	6	7	1	7	8	7
25	3	4	2	2	9	1	9	0	7	8	1	6	2	5	3	9	0	9	1	0
26	2	7	3	9	5	9	9	3	2	9	3	9	1	9	0	5	5	1	4	2
27	0	2	5	4	0	8	1	7	0	7	1	3	0	4	3	0	6	4	4	4
28	8	6	0	5	4	8	8	2	7	7	0	1	0	1	7	1	3	5	3	4
29	4	2	6	4	5	2	4	2	6	1	7	5	6	6	4	0	8	4	1	2
30	4	4	9	8	7	3	4	3	8	2	9	1	5	3	5	9	8	9	2	9
31	6	4	8	0	0	0	4	2	3	8	1	8	4	0	9	5	0	9	0	4
32	3	2	3	8	4	8	8	6	2	9	1	0	1	9	9	3	0	7	3	5
33	6	6	7	2	8	0	0	8	4	0	0	4	6	0	3	2	2	4	6	8
34	8	0	3	1	1	1	1	2	7	0	1	9	1	2	7	1	3	3	5	3
35	5	3	5	7	3	6	3	1	7	2	5	5	1	4	7	1	6	5	6	5
36	9	1	1	9	2	8	3	0	3	6	7	7	4	7	5	9	8	1	8	3
37	9	0	2	9	9	7	4	6	3	6	6	3	7	4	2	7	0	0	1	9
38	8	1	4	6	4	6	8	2	8	9	5	5	2	9	6	2	5	3	0	3
39	4	1	1	9	7	0	7	2	9	0	9	7	0	4	6	2	3	1	0	9
40	9	9	2	7	1	3	2	9	0	3	9	0	7	5	6	7	1	7	8	7

ID	Travel to School	Favorite Season	Allergies	Favorite School Subject	Favorite Music	Superpower
1	Car	Spring	Yes	English	Pop	Freeze time
2	Car	Summer	Yes	Music	Pop	Telepathy
3	Car	Summer	No	Science	Pop	Fly
4	Walk	Fall	No	Computers and technology	Pop	Invisibility
5	Car	Summer	No	Art	Country	Telepathy
6	Car	Summer	No	Physical education	Rap/Hip-hop	Freeze time
7	Car	Spring	No	Physical education	Pop	Telepathy
8	Car	Winter	No	Art	Other	Fly
9	Car	Summer	No	Physical education	Pop	Fly
10	Car	Spring	No	Mathematics and statistics	Pop	Telepathy
11	Car	Summer	Yes	History	Rap/Hip-hop	Invisibility
12	Car	Spring	No	Art	Rap/Hip-hop	Freeze time
13	Bus	Winter	No	Computers and technology	Rap/Hip-hop	Fly
14	Car	Winter	Yes	Social studies	Rap/Hip-hop	Fly
15	Car	Summer	No	Art	Pop	Freeze time
16	Car	Fall	No	Mathematics and statistics	Pop	Fly
17	Bus	Winter	No	Science	Rap/Hip-hop	Freeze time
18	Car	Spring	Yes	Art	Pop	Telepathy
19	Car	Fall	Yes	Science	Pop	Telepathy
20	Car	Summer	Yes	Physical education	Rap/Hip-hop	Invisibility
21	Car	Spring	Yes	Science	Pop	Invisibility
22	Car	Winter	Yes	Mathematics and statistics	Country	Invisibility
23	Car	Summer	Yes	Art	Pop	Invisibility
24	Bus	Winter	Yes	Other	Pop	Telepathy
25	Bus	Summer	Yes	Science	Other	Fly
26	Car	Summer	No	Science	Pop	Fly
27	Car	Summer	Yes	Music	Pop	Telepathy
28	Car	Summer	No	Physical education	Country	Super strength
29	Car	Fall	Yes	Mathematics and statistics	Country	Telepathy
30	Car	Summer	Yes	Physical education	Rap/Hip-hop	Telepathy
31	Boat	Winter	No	Computers and technology	Gospel	Invisibility
32	Car	Spring	No	Physical education	Pop	Fly
33	Car	Spring	No	Physical education	Pop	Fly
34	Car	Summer	No	Mathematics and statistics	Classical	Fly
35	Car	Fall	Yes	Science	Jazz	Telepathy
36	Car	Spring	No	Science	Rap/Hip-hop	Telepathy
37	Car	Summer	No	Music	Country	Telepathy
38	Bus	Winter	No	Mathematics and statistics	Pop	Fly
39	Car	Spring	No	Art	Classical	Freeze time
40	Car	Winter	Yes	Art	Pop	Fly
41	Walk	Summer	Yes	Physical education	Rap/Hip-hop	Fly
42	Bus	Winter	Yes	Physical education	Gospel	Invisibility

Lesson 20:   Estimating a Population Proportion

EUREKA MATH

43	Bus	Summer	No	Art	Other	Invisibility
44	Car	Summer	Yes	Computers and technology	Other	Freeze time
45	Car	Fall	Yes	Science	Pop	Fly
46	Car	Summer	Yes	Music	Rap/Hip-hop	Fly
47	Car	Spring	No	Science	Rap/Hip-hop	Invisibility
48	Bus	Spring	No	Music	Pop	Telepathy
49	Car	Summer	Yes	Social studies	Techno/Electronic	Telepathy
50	Car	Summer	Yes	Physical education	Pop	Telepathy
51	Car	Spring	Yes	Other	Other	Telepathy
52	Car	Summer	No	Art	Pop	Fly
53	Car	Summer	Yes	Other	Pop	Telepathy
54	Car	Summer	Yes	Physical education	Rap/Hip-hop	Invisibility
55	Bus	Summer	Yes	Physical education	Other	Super strength
56	Car	Summer	No	Science	Rap/Hip-hop	Invisibility
57	Car	Winter	No	Languages	Rap/Hip-hop	Super strength
58	Car	Fall	Yes	English	Pop	Fly
59	Car	Winter	No	Science	Pop	Telepathy
60	Car	Summer	No	Art	Pop	Invisibility
61	Car	Summer	Yes	Other	Pop	Freeze time
62	Bus	Spring	No	Science	Pop	Fly
63	Car	Winter	Yes	Mathematics and statistics	Other	Freeze time
64	Car	Summer	No	Social studies	Classical	Fly
65	Car	Winter	Yes	Science	Pop	Telepathy
66	Car	Winter	No	Science	Rock and roll	Fly
67	Car	Summer	No	Mathematics and statistics	Rap/Hip-hop	Super strength
68	Car	Fall	No	Music	Rock and roll	Super strength
69	Car	Spring	No	Other	Other	Invisibility
70	Car	Summer	Yes	Mathematics and statistics	Rap/Hip-hop	Telepathy
71	Car	Winter	No	Art	Other	Fly
72	Car	Spring	Yes	Mathematics and statistics	Pop	Telepathy
73	Car	Winter	Yes	Computers and technology	Techno/Electronic	Telepathy
74	Walk	Winter	No	Physical education	Techno/Electronic	Fly
75	Walk	Summer	No	History	Rock and roll	Fly
76	Skateboard/ Scooter/ Rollerblade	Winter	Yes	Computers and technology	Techno/Electronic	Freeze time
77	Car	Spring	Yes	Science	Other	Telepathy
78	Car	Summer	No	Music	Rap/Hip-hop	Invisibility
79	Car	Summer	No	Social studies	Pop	Invisibility
80	Car	Summer	No	Other	Rap/Hip-hop	Telepathy
81	Walk	Spring	Yes	History	Rap/Hip-hop	Invisibility
82	Car	Summer	No	Art	Pop	Invisibility

Lesson 20:   Estimating a Population Proportion

249

83	Walk	Spring	No	Languages	Jazz	Super strength
84	Car	Fall	No	History	Jazz	Invisibility
85	Car	Summer	No	Physical education	Rap/Hip-hop	Freeze time
86	Car	Spring	No	Mathematics and statistics	Pop	Freeze time
87	Bus	Spring	Yes	Art	Pop	Telepathy
88	Car	Winter	No	Mathematics and statistics	Other	Invisibility
89	Car	Summer	Yes	Physical education	Country	Telepathy
90	Bus	Summer	No	Computers and technology	Other	Fly
91	Car	Winter	No	History	Pop	Telepathy
92	Walk	Winter	No	Science	Classical	Telepathy
93	Bicycle	Summer	No	Physical education	Pop	Invisibility
94	Car	Summer	No	English	Pop	Telepathy
95	Car	Summer	Yes	Physical education	Pop	Fly
96	Car	Winter	No	Science	Other	Freeze time
97	Car	Winter	No	Other	Rap/Hip-hop	Super strength
98	Car	Summer	Yes	Physical education	Rap/Hip-hop	Freeze time
99	Car	Spring	No	Music	Classical	Telepathy
100	Car	Spring	Yes	Science	Gospel	Telepathy
101	Car	Summer	Yes	History	Pop	Super strength
102	Car	Winter	Yes	English	Country	Freeze time
103	Car	Spring	No	Computers and technology	Other	Telepathy
104	Car	Winter	No	History	Other	Invisibility
105	Car	Fall	No	Music	Pop	Telepathy
106	Car	Fall	No	Science	Pop	Telepathy
107	Car	Winter	No	Art	Heavy metal	Fly
108	Car	Spring	Yes	Science	Rock and roll	Fly
109	Car	Fall	Yes	Music	Other	Fly
110	Car	Summer	Yes	Social studies	Techno/Electronic	Telepathy
111	Car	Spring	No	Physical education	Pop	Fly
112	Car	Summer	No	Physical education	Pop	Fly
113	Car	Summer	Yes	Social studies	Pop	Freeze time
114	Car	Summer	Yes	Computers and technology	Gospel	Freeze time
115	Car	Winter	Yes	Other	Rap/Hip-hop	Telepathy
116	Car	Summer	Yes	Science	Country	Telepathy
117	Car	Fall		Music	Country	Fly
118	Walk	Summer	No	History	Pop	Telepathy
119	Car	Spring	Yes	Art	Pop	Freeze time
120	Car	Fall	Yes	Physical education	Rap/Hip-hop	Fly
121	Car	Spring	No	Music	Rock and roll	Telepathy
122	Car	Fall	No	Art	Pop	Invisibility
123	Car	Summer	Yes	Physical education	Rap/Hip-hop	Fly
124	Walk	Summer	No	Computers and technology	Pop	Telepathy
125	Car	Fall	No	Art	Pop	Fly

Lesson 20:   Estimating a Population Proportion

EUREKA MATH®

126	Bicycle	Spring	No	Science	Pop	Invisibility
127	Car	Summer	No	Social studies	Gospel	Fly
128	Bicycle	Winter	No	Social studies	Rap/Hip-hop	Fly
129	Car	Summer	Yes	Mathematics and statistics	Pop	Invisibility
130	Car	Fall	Yes	Mathematics and statistics	Country	Telepathy
131	Car	Winter	Yes	Music	Gospel	Super strength
132	Rail (Train/ Tram/Subway)	Fall	Yes	Art	Other	Fly
133	Walk	Summer	No	Social studies	Pop	Invisibility
134	Car	Summer	Yes	Music	Pop	Freeze time
135	Car	Winter	No	Mathematics and statistics	Pop	Telepathy
136	Car	Fall	Yes	Music	Pop	Telepathy
137	Car	Summer	Yes	Computers and technology	Other	Freeze time
138	Car	Summer	Yes	Physical education	Pop	Telepathy
139	Car	Summer	Yes	Social studies	Other	Telepathy
140	Car	Spring	Yes	Physical education	Other	Freeze time
141	Car	Fall	Yes	Science	Country	Telepathy
142	Car	Spring	Yes	Science	Pop	Invisibility
143	Car	Summer	No	Other	Rap/Hip-hop	Freeze time
144	Car	Summer	No	Other	Other	Fly
145	Car	Summer	No	Languages	Pop	Freeze time
146	Car	Summer	Yes	Physical education	Pop	Telepathy
147	Bus	Winter	No	History	Country	Invisibility
148	Car	Spring	No	Computers and technology	Other	Telepathy
149	Bus	Winter	Yes	Science	Pop	Invisibility
150	Car	Summer	No	Social studies	Rap/Hip-hop	Invisibility
151	Car	Summer	No	Physical education	Pop	Invisibility
152	Car	Summer	Yes	Physical education	Pop	Super strength
153	Car	Summer	No	Mathematics and statistics	Pop	Fly
154	Car	Summer	No	Art	Rap/Hip-hop	Freeze time
155	Car	Winter	Yes	Other	Classical	Freeze time
156	Car	Summer	Yes	Computers and technology	Other	Telepathy
157	Car	Spring	No	Other	Pop	Freeze time
158	Car	Winter	Yes	Music	Country	Fly
159	Car	Winter	No	History	Jazz	Invisibility
160	Car	Spring	Yes	History	Pop	Fly
161	Car	Winter	Yes	Mathematics and statistics	Other	Telepathy
162	Car	Fall	No	Science	Country	Invisibility
163	Car	Winter	No	Science	Other	Fly
164	Car	Summer	No	Science	Pop	Fly
165	Skateboard/ Scooter/ Rollerblade	Spring	Yes	Social studies	Other	Freeze time
166	Car	Winter	Yes	Art	Rap/Hip-hop	Fly

Lesson 20: Estimating a Population Proportion

167	Car	Summer	Yes	Other	Pop	Freeze time
168	Car	Summer	No	English	Pop	Telepathy
169	Car	Summer	No	Other	Pop	Invisibility
170	Car	Summer	Yes	Physical education	Techno/Electronic	Freeze time
171	Car	Summer	No	Art	Pop	Telepathy
172	Car	Summer	No	Physical education	Rap/Hip-hop	Freeze time
173	Car	Winter	Yes	Mathematics and statistics	Other	Invisibility
174	Bus	Summer	Yes	Music	Pop	Freeze time
175	Car	Winter	No	Art	Pop	Fly
176	Car	Fall	No	Science	Rap/Hip-hop	Fly
177	Car	Winter	Yes	Social studies	Pop	Telepathy
178	Car	Fall	No	Art	Other	Fly
179	Bus	Spring	No	Physical education	Country	Fly
180	Car	Winter	No	Music	Other	Telepathy
181	Bus	Summer	No	Computers and technology	Rap/Hip-hop	Freeze time
182	Car	Summer	Yes	Physical education	Rap/Hip-hop	Invisibility
183	Car	Summer	Yes	Music	Other	Telepathy
184	Car	Spring	No	Science	Rap/Hip-hop	Invisibility
185	Rail (Train/ Tram/Subway)	Summer	No	Physical education	Other	Freeze time
186	Car	Summer	Yes	Mathematics and statistics	Rap/Hip-hop	Fly
187	Bus	Winter	Yes	Mathematics and statistics	Other	Super strength
188	Car	Summer	No	Mathematics and statistics	Other	Freeze time
189	Rail (Train/ Tram/Subway)	Fall	Yes	Music	Jazz	Fly
190	Car	Summer	Yes	Science	Pop	Super strength
191	Car	Summer	Yes	Science	Techno/Electronic	Freeze time
192	Car	Spring	Yes	Physical education	Rap/Hip-hop	Freeze time
193	Car	Summer	Yes	Physical education	Rap/Hip-hop	Freeze time
194	Car	Winter	No	Physical education	Rap/Hip-hop	Telepathy
195	Car	Winter	No	Music	Jazz	Freeze time
196	Walk	Summer	Yes	History	Country	Freeze time
197	Car	Spring	No	History	Rap/Hip-hop	Freeze time
198	Car	Fall	Yes	Other	Pop	Freeze time
199	Car	Spring	Yes	Science	Other	Freeze time
200	Bicycle	Winter	Yes	Other	Rap/Hip-hop	Freeze time

Name _____ Date _____

Thirty seventh graders each took a random sample of 10 middle school students and asked each student whether or not he likes pop music. Then, they calculated the proportion of students who like pop music for each sample. The dot plot below shows the distribution of the sample proportions.

Dot Plot of Sample Proportions for n = 10

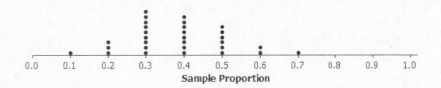

1. There are three dots above 0.2. What does each dot represent in terms of this scenario?

2. Based on the dot plot, do you think the proportion of the middle school students at this school who like pop music is 0.6? Explain why or why not.

A group of 20 seventh graders wanted to estimate the proportion of middle school students who buy school lunch every day. Each seventh grader took a random sample of 20 middle school students and asked each student whether or not he or she bought lunch. Following are the sample proportions the seventh graders found in 20 samples.

0.15	0.10	0.20	0.00	0.05
0.25	0.30	0.00	0.10	0.15
0.10	0.05	0.20	0.10	0.10
0.15	0.15	0.20	0.00	0.10

> I can write this number as a fraction, $\frac{25}{100}$. To determine how many students in the sample buy school lunch every day, I find an equivalent fraction where the denominator is the sample size.

1. One of the seventh graders reported a sample proportion of 0.25. What does this value mean in terms of the scenario?

$$\frac{25}{100} = \frac{5}{20}$$

A sample proportion of 0.25 means that 5 out of 20 students in the sample buy school lunch every day.

2. Construct a dot plot of the 20 sample proportions.

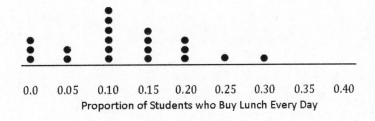

3. Describe the shape of the distribution.

    ***The shape of the distribution is symmetric.
    It centers at approximately*** 0.10.

    > A majority of the data values center around the
    > same number. I notice the dot plot looks like a
    > mound, so it would have a symmetric shape.

4. Using the 20 sample proportions listed above, what is your estimate for the proportion of all the middle
    school students who bought school lunch every day?

    My estimate for the proportion of all middle school students who bought school lunch every day is 0.12
    because I think the proportion will be between 0.10 ***and*** 0.15.

    > Answers will vary but
    > should be close to the
    > actual mean of 0.1225.

1. A class of 30 seventh graders wanted to estimate the proportion of middle school students who played a musical instrument. Each seventh grader took a random sample of 25 middle school students and asked each student whether or not she played a musical instrument. The following are the sample proportions the seventh graders found in 30 samples.

    | 0.80 | 0.64 | 0.72 | 0.60 | 0.60 | 0.72 | 0.76 | 0.68 | 0.72 | 0.68 |
    | 0.72 | 0.68 | 0.68 | 0.76 | 0.84 | 0.60 | 0.80 | 0.72 | 0.76 | 0.80 |
    | 0.76 | 0.60 | 0.80 | 0.84 | 0.68 | 0.68 | 0.70 | 0.68 | 0.64 | 0.72 |

    a. The first student reported a sample proportion of 0.80. What does this value mean in terms of this scenario?

    b. Construct a dot plot of the 30 sample proportions.

    c. Describe the shape of the distribution.

    d. Describe the variability of the distribution.

    e. Using the 30 class sample proportions listed above, what is your estimate for the proportion of all middle school students who played a musical instrument?

2. Select another variable or column from the data file that is of interest. Take a random sample of 30 students from the list, and record the response to your variable of interest of each of the 30 students.

    a. Based on your random sample, what is your estimate for the proportion of all middle school students?

    b. If you selected a second random sample of 30, would you get the same sample proportion for the second random sample that you got for the first random sample? Explain why or why not.

There are three bags, Bag A, Bag B, and Bag C, with 100 numbers in each bag. You and your classmates will investigate the population mean (the mean of all 100 numbers) in each bag. Each set of numbers has the same range. However, the population means of each set may or may not be the same. We will see who can uncover the mystery of the bags!

Exercises

1. To begin your investigation, start by selecting a random sample of ten numbers from Bag A. Remember to mix the numbers in the bag first. Then, select one number from the bag. Do not put it back into the bag. Write the number in the chart below. Continue selecting one number at a time until you have selected ten numbers. Mix up the numbers in the bag between each selection.

Selection	1	2	3	4	5	6	7	8	9	10
Bag A										

a. Create a dot plot of your sample of ten numbers. Use a dot to represent each number in the sample.

b. Do you think the mean of all the numbers in Bag A might be 10? Why or why not?

c. Based on the dot plot, what would you estimate the mean of the numbers in Bag A to be? How did you make your estimate?

d. Do you think your sample mean will be close to the population mean? Why or why not?

e.   Is your sample mean the same as your neighbors' sample means? Why or why not?

2.   Repeat the process by selecting a random sample of ten numbers from Bag B.

Selection	1	2	3	4	5	6	7	8	9	10
Bag B										

a.   Create a dot plot of your sample of ten numbers. Use a dot to represent each of the numbers in the sample.

b.   Based on your dot plot, do you think the mean of the numbers in Bag B is the same or different from the mean of the numbers in Bag A? Explain your thinking.

3.   Repeat the process once more by selecting a random sample of ten numbers from Bag C.

Selection	1	2	3	4	5	6	7	8	9	10
Bag C										

a.   Create a dot plot of your sample of ten numbers. Use a dot to represent each of the numbers in the sample.

b.   Based on your dot plot, do you think the mean of the numbers in Bag C is the same as or different from the mean of the numbers in Bag A? Explain your thinking.

4. Are your dot plots of the three bags the same as the dot plots of other students in your class? Why or why not?

5. Calculate the mean of the numbers for each of the samples from Bag A, Bag B, and Bag C.

	Mean of the Sample of Numbers
Bag A	
Bag B	
Bag C	

a. Are the sample means you calculated the same as the sample means of other members of your class? Why or why not?

b. How do your sample means for Bag A and for Bag B compare?

c. Calculate the difference of the sample mean for Bag A minus the sample mean for Bag B (Mean A – Mean B). Based on this difference, can you be sure which bag has the larger population mean? Why or why not?

6. Based on the class dot plots of the sample means, do you think the mean of the numbers in Bag A and the mean of the numbers in Bag B are different? Do you think the mean of the numbers in Bag A and the mean of the numbers in Bag C are different? Explain your answers.

7. Based on the difference between the sample mean of Bag A and the sample mean of Bag B (Mean A – Mean B) that you calculated in Exercise 5, do you think that the two populations (Bags A and B) have different means, or do you think that the two population means might be the same?

8. Based on this difference, can you be sure which bag has the larger population mean? Why or why not?

9. Is your difference in sample means the same as your neighbors' differences? Why or why not?

10. Plot your difference of the means (Mean A – Mean B) on a class dot plot. Describe the distribution of differences plotted on the graph. Remember to discuss center and spread.

11. Why are the differences in the sample means of Bag A and Bag B not always 0?

12. Does the class dot plot contain differences that were relatively far away from 0? If yes, why do you think this happened?

EUREKA MATH®

13. Suppose you will take a sample from a new bag. How big would the difference in the sample mean for Bag A and the sample mean for the new bag (Mean A – Mean new) have to be before you would be convinced that the population mean for the new bag is different from the population mean of Bag A? Use the class dot plot of the differences in sample means for Bags A and B (which have equal population means) to help you answer this question.

The differences in the class dot plot occur because of sampling variability—the chance variability from one sample to another. In Exercise 13, you were asked about how great the difference in sample means would need to be before you have convincing evidence that one population mean is larger than another population mean. A *meaningful* difference between two sample means is one that is unlikely to have occurred by chance if the population means are equal. In other words, the difference is one that is greater than would have been expected just due to sampling variability.

14. Calculate the sample mean of Bag A minus the sample mean of Bag C (Mean A – Mean C).

15. Plot your difference (Mean A – Mean C) on a class dot plot.

16. How do the centers of the class dot plots for Mean A – Mean B and Mean A – Mean C compare?

17. Each bag has a population mean that is either 10.5 or 14.5. State what you think the population mean is for each bag. Explain your choice for each bag.

Lesson Summary

- Remember to think about sampling variability—the chance variability from sample to sample.

- Beware of making decisions based just on the fact that two sample means are not equal.

- Consider the distribution of the difference in sample means when making a decision.

Lesson 21: Why Worry About Sampling Variability?

Name _____   Date _____

How is a *meaningful* difference in sample means different from a *non-meaningful* difference in sample means? You may use what you saw in the dot plots of this lesson to help you answer this question.

Below are two dot plots. Each dot plot represents the differences in sample means for random samples selected from two populations (Bag A and Bag B). For each distribution, the differences were found by subtracting the sample means of Bag B from the sample means of Bag A (sample mean A – sample mean B).

1. Examine the dot plot below.

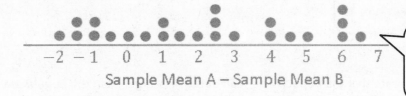

Sample Mean A – Sample Mean B

> I notice that a majority of the differences are a positive value.

a. Does the dot plot above indicate that the population mean of Bag A is larger than the population mean of Bag B? Why or why not?

The population mean of Bag A is larger than the population mean of Bag B because a majority of the differences are positive, which means the sample means for Bag A were larger than the sample means for Bag B.

> Due to the order of the subtraction, if the population mean of Bag B were bigger than Bag A, a majority of the differences would be negative.

b. In the dot plot above, how many differences are greater than 0? How many differences are less than 0? What might this tell you?

There are 17 differences that are greater than 0 and only 6 differences that are less than 0. This would tell me that the population mean for Bag A is most likely larger than the population mean for Bag B because a larger number minus a smaller number results in a positive number.

> It is possible that the population mean of Bag B is larger than the population mean of Bag A, but it is not very likely since there are a lot more positive differences than negative differences.

2. Examine the dot plot below.

The dot plot is centered around 0, so I expect that the difference of the two population means is also close to 0.

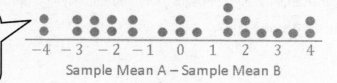

Sample Mean A – Sample Mean B

Does the dot plot above indicate that the population mean of Bag A is larger than the population mean of Bag B? Why or why not?

The dot plot indicates that the population means of both bags are about the same because there are the same number of positive and negative values on the dot plot.

EUREKA
MATH

Below are three dot plots. Each dot plot represents the differences in sample means for random samples selected from two populations (Bag A and Bag B). For each distribution, the differences were found by subtracting the sample means of Bag B from the sample means of Bag A (sample mean A – sample mean B).

1. Does the graph below indicate that the population mean of Bag A is larger than the population mean of Bag B? Why or why not?

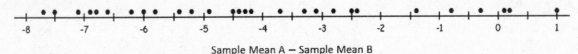

Sample Mean A – Sample Mean B

2. Use the graph above to estimate the difference in the population means (Mean A – Mean B).

3. Does the graph below indicate that the population mean of Bag A is larger than the population mean of Bag B? Why or why not?

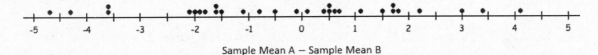

Sample Mean A – Sample Mean B

4. Does the graph below indicate that the population mean of Bag A is larger than the population mean of Bag B? Why or why not?

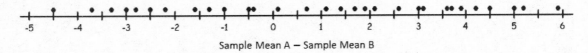

Sample Mean A – Sample Mean B

5. In the above graph, how many differences are greater than 0? How many differences are less than 0? What might this tell you?

6. In Problem 4, the population mean for Bag A is really larger than the population mean for Bag B. Why is it possible to still get so many negative differences in the graph?

In previous lessons, you worked with one population. Many statistical questions involve comparing two populations. For example:

- On average, do boys and girls differ on quantitative reasoning?
- Do students learn basic arithmetic skills better with or without calculators?
- Which of two medications is more effective in treating migraine headaches?
- Does one type of car get better mileage per gallon of gasoline than another type?
- Does one type of fabric decay in landfills faster than another type?
- Do people with diabetes heal more slowly than people who do not have diabetes?

In this lesson, you will begin to explore how big of a difference there needs to be in sample means in order for the difference to be considered meaningful. The next lesson will extend that understanding to making informal inferences about population differences.

Examples 1–3

Tamika's mathematics project is to see whether boys or girls are faster in solving a KenKen-type puzzle. She creates a puzzle and records the following times that it took to solve the puzzle (in seconds) for a random sample of 10 boys from her school and a random sample of 11 girls from her school:

												Mean	MAD
Boys	39	38	27	36	40	27	43	36	34	33		35.3	4.04
Girls	41	41	33	42	47	38	41	36	36	32	46	39.4	3.96

1. On the same scale, draw dot plots for the boys' data and for the girls' data. Comment on the amount of overlap between the two dot plots. How are the dot plots the same, and how are they different?

2. Compare the variability in the two data sets using the MAD (mean absolute deviation). Is the variability in each sample about the same? Interpret the MAD in the context of the problem.

3. In the previous lesson, you learned that a difference between two sample means is considered to be meaningful if the difference is more than what you would expect to see just based on sampling variability. The difference in the sample means of the boys' times and the girls' times is 4.1 seconds (39.4 seconds – 35.3 seconds). This difference is approximately 1 MAD.

    a. If 4 sec. is used to approximate the values of 1 MAD for both boys and for girls, what is the interval of times that are within 1 MAD of the sample mean for boys?

    b. Of the 10 sample means for boys, how many of them are within that interval?

    c. Of the 11 sample means for girls, how many of them are within the interval you calculated in part (a)?

    d. Based on the dot plots, do you think that the difference between the two sample means is a meaningful difference? That is, are you convinced that the mean time for all girls at the school (not just this sample of girls) is different from the mean time for all boys at the school? Explain your choice based on the dot plots.

EUREKA
MATH

Examples 4–7

How good are you at estimating a minute? Work in pairs. Flip a coin to determine which person in the pair will go first. One of you puts your head down and raises your hand. When your partner says "Start," keep your head down and your hand raised. When you think a minute is up, put your hand down. Your partner will record how much time has passed. Note that the room needs to be quiet. Switch roles, except this time you talk with your partner during the period when the person with his head down is indicating when he thinks a minute is up. Note that the room will not be quiet.

Group	Estimate for a Minute													
Quiet														
Talking														

Use your class data to complete the following.

4.   Calculate the mean minute time for each group. Then, find the difference between the *quiet* mean and the *talking* mean.

5.   On the same scale, draw dot plots of the two data distributions, and discuss the similarities and differences in the two distributions.

6. Calculate the mean absolute deviation (MAD) for each data set. Based on the MADs, compare the variability in each sample. Is the variability about the same? Interpret the MADs in the context of the problem.

7. Based on your calculations, is the difference in mean time estimates meaningful? Part of your reasoning should involve the number of MADs that separate the two sample means. Note that if the MADs differ, use the larger one in determining how many MADs separate the two means.

Lesson 22:   Using Sample Data to Compare the Means of
Two or More Populations

EUREKA
MATH

Lesson Summary

Variability is a natural occurrence in data distributions. Two data distributions can be compared by describing how far apart their sample means are. The amount of separation can be measured in terms of how many MADs separate the means. (Note that if the two sample MADs differ, the larger of the two is used to make this calculation.)

Name _____   Date _____

Suppose that Brett randomly sampled 12 tenth-grade girls and boys in his school district and asked them for the number of minutes per day that they text. The data and summary measures follow.

Gender	Number of Minutes of Texting												Mean	MAD
Girls	98	104	95	101	98	107	86	92	96	107	88	95	97.3	5.3
Boys	66	72	65	60	78	82	63	56	85	79	68	77	70.9	7.9

1. Draw dot plots for the two data sets using the same numerical scales. Discuss the amount of overlap between the two dot plots that you drew and what it may mean in the context of the problem.

2. Compare the variability in the two data sets using the MAD. Interpret the result in the context of the problem.

3. From 1 and 2, does the difference in the two means appear to be meaningful? Explain.

Measure of Variability

1. A school is trying to decide which math program to purchase.

   a. How many mean absolute deviations (MADs) separate the mean mathematics score for the Math Facts program (mean = 47.7, MAD = 3.7, $n = 32$) and the Math Genius program (mean = 38.6, MAD = 4.0, $n = 28$)?

$$\frac{47.7 - 38.6}{4.0} = 2.275$$

> I subtract the two sample means and then divide by the MAD. If the two MADs are different, I use the larger of the two MADs.

> This value indicates that the data are separated by a little more than 2 MADs.

The number of MADs that separate the sample mean mathematics score for the Math Facts program and the Math Genius program is 2.275, a little more than two MADs.

   b. What recommendation would you make based on the result?

The number of MADs that separate the two programs is significant, so I would recommend the Math Facts program because it produces higher scores.

> I know Math Facts produces significantly higher scores because the mean is higher than the Math Genius mean.

> In general, if the MADs are separated by 2 or more, then this is significant.

2. Does a pickup truck or an SUV get better gas mileage? A sample of 10 different cars and pickup trucks and their gas mileage (miles per gallon) is provided in the table below.

Trucks	16	15	19	18	18	21	17	19	20	20
SUVs	20	20	20	23	25	23	24	22	30	26

a. Calculate the difference between the sample mean gas mileage for the trucks and for the SUVs.

Sample mean gas mileage (in miles per gallon) for trucks:

$$\frac{16 + 15 + 19 + 18 + 18 + 21 + 17 + 19 + 20 + 20}{10} = 18.3$$

> To calculate the mean, I add my data values together and divide by the number of data values.

Sample mean gas mileage (in miles per gallon) for SUVs:

$$\frac{20 + 20 + 20 + 23 + 25 + 23 + 24 + 22 + 30 + 26}{10} = 23.3$$

23.3 − 18.3 = 5

The difference between the two sample means is 5.

b. On the same scale, draw dot plots of the two distributions, and discuss the variability in each distribution.

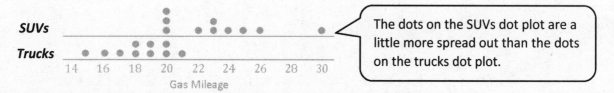

> The dots on the SUVs dot plot are a little more spread out than the dots on the trucks dot plot.

The SUVs have a little larger variability than the trucks.

EUREKA
MATH

To calculate the MAD, I first need to determine the deviations or the distance each point is from the mean.

c. Calculate the MAD for each distribution. Based on the MADs, compare the variability in each distribution. Is the variability about the same? Interpret the MADs in the context of the problem.

Deviations of Trucks:

$18.3 - 16 = 2.3$

$18.3 - 15 = 3.3$

$19 - 18.3 = 0.7$

Now that I know the deviations, I find the sum of the deviations and divide the sum by the number of data values.

$18.3 - 18 = 0.3$ $\dfrac{2.3 + 3.3 + 0.7 + 0.3 + 0.3 + 2.7 + 1.3 + 0.7 + 1.7 + 1.7}{10} = \dfrac{15}{10} = 1.5$

$18.3 - 18 = 0.3$

$21 - 18.3 = 2.7$

$18.3 - 17 = 1.3$

$19 - 18.3 = 0.7$

$20 - 18.3 = 1.7$

$20 - 18.3 = 1.7$

I follow the same process to calculate the MAD for SUVs.

SUVs:

$$\dfrac{3.3 + 3.3 + 3.3 + 0.3 + 1.7 + 0.3 + 0.7 + 1.3 + 6.7 + 2.7}{10} = \dfrac{23.6}{10} = 2.36$$

The MAD for trucks is 1.5, which means the typical deviation from the mean of 18.3 is 1.5.

The MAD for SUVs is 2.36, which means the typical deviation from the mean of 23.3 is 2.36.

d. Based on your calculations, is the difference in mean distance meaningful?

$\dfrac{5}{2.36} \approx 2.11$

There is a separation of approximately 2.11 MADs. There is a meaningful distance between the means.

I know a meaningful distance is similar to a significant difference.

1. A school is trying to decide which reading program to purchase.

   a. How many MADs separate the mean reading comprehension score for a standard program (mean = 67.8, MAD = 4.6, $n = 24$) and an activity-based program (mean = 70.3, MAD = 4.5, $n = 27$)?

   b. What recommendation would you make based on this result?

2. Does a football filled with helium go farther than one filled with air? Two identical footballs were used: one filled with helium and one filled with air to the same pressure. Matt was chosen from your team to do the kicking. You did not tell Matt which ball he was kicking. The data (in yards) follow.

Air	25	23	28	29	27	32	24	26	22	27	31	24	33	26	24	28	30
Helium	24	19	25	25	22	24	28	31	22	26	24	23	22	21	21	23	25

	Mean	MAD
Air		
Helium		

   a. Calculate the difference between the sample mean distance for the football filled with air and for the one filled with helium.

   b. On the same scale, draw dot plots of the two distributions, and discuss the variability in each distribution.

   c. Calculate the MAD for each distribution. Based on the MADs, compare the variability in each distribution. Is the variability about the same? Interpret the MADs in the context of the problem.

   d. Based on your calculations, is the difference in mean distance meaningful? Part of your reasoning should involve the number of MADs that separate the sample means. Note that if the MADs differ, use the larger one in determining how many MADs separate the two means.

3. Suppose that your classmates were debating about whether going to college is really worth it. Based on the following data of annual salaries (rounded to the nearest thousands of dollars) for college graduates and high school graduates with no college experience, does it appear that going to college is indeed worth the effort? The data are from people in their second year of employment.

College Grad	41	67	53	48	45	60	59	55	52	52	50	59	44	49	52
High School Grad	23	33	36	29	25	43	42	38	27	25	33	41	29	33	35

   a. Calculate the difference between the sample mean salary for college graduates and for high school graduates.

   b. On the same scale, draw dot plots of the two distributions, and discuss the variability in each distribution.

   c. Calculate the MAD for each distribution. Based on the MADs, compare the variability in each distribution. Is the variability about the same? Interpret the MADs in the context of the problem.

   d. Based on your calculations, is going to college worth the effort? Part of your reasoning should involve the number of MADs that separate the sample means.

In the previous lesson, you described how far apart the means of two data sets are in terms of the MAD (mean absolute deviation), a measure of variability. In this lesson, you will extend that idea to informally determine when two sample means computed from random samples are far enough apart from each other to imply that the population means also differ in a *meaningful* way. Recall that a *meaningful* difference between two means is a difference that is greater than would have been expected just due to sampling variability.

Example 1: Texting

With texting becoming so popular, Linda wanted to determine if middle school students memorize *real* words more or less easily than *fake* words. For example, real words are *food, car, study, swim*, whereas fake words are *stk, fonw, cqur, ttnsp*. She randomly selected 28 students from all middle school students in her district and gave half of them a list of 20 real words and the other half a list of 20 fake words.

    a.   How do you think Linda might have randomly selected 28 students from all middle school students in her district?

    b.   Why do you think Linda selected the students for her study randomly? Explain.

c. She gave the selected students one minute to memorize their lists, after which they were to turn the lists over and, after two minutes, write down all the words that they could remember. Afterward, they calculated the number of correct words that they were able to write down. Do you think a penalty should be given for an incorrect word written down? Explain your reasoning.

Exercises 1–4

Suppose the data (the number of correct words recalled) she collected were as follows:

For students given the real words list: 8, 11, 12, 8, 4, 7, 9, 12, 12, 9, 14, 11, 5, 10

For students given the fake words list: 3, 5, 4, 4, 4, 7, 11, 9, 7, 7, 1, 3, 3, 7

1. On the same scale, draw dot plots for the two data sets.

2. From looking at the dot plots, write a few sentences comparing the distribution of the number of correctly recalled real words with the distribution of the number of correctly recalled fake words. In particular, comment on which type of word, if either, that students recall better. Explain.

EUREKA MATH

3. Linda made the following calculations for the two data sets:

	Mean	MAD
Real Words Recalled	9.43	2.29
Fake Words Recalled	5.36	2.27

In the previous lesson, you calculated the number of MADs that separated two sample means. You used the larger MAD to make this calculation if the two MADs were not the same. How many MADs separate the mean number of real words recalled and the mean number of fake words recalled for the students in the study?

4. In the last lesson, our work suggested that if the number of MADs that separate the two sample means is 2 or more, then it is reasonable to conclude that not only do the means differ in the samples but that the means differ in the populations as well. If the number of MADs is less than 2, then you can conclude that the difference in the sample means might just be sampling variability and that there may not be a meaningful difference in the population means. Using these criteria, what can Linda conclude about the difference in population means based on the sample data that she collected? Be sure to express your conclusion in the context of this problem.

Example 2

Ken, an eighth-grade student, was interested in doing a statistics study involving sixth-grade and eleventh-grade students in his school district. He conducted a survey on four numerical variables and two categorical variables (grade level and gender). His Excel population database for the 265 sixth graders and 175 eleventh graders in his district has the following description:

Column	Name	Description
1	ID	ID numbers are from 1 through 440.
		1–128 sixth-grade females
		129–265 sixth-grade males
		266–363 eleventh-grade females
		364–440 eleventh-grade males
2	Texting	Number of minutes per day texting (whole number)
3	ReacTime	Time in seconds to respond to a computer screen stimulus (two decimal places)
4	Homework	Total number of hours per week spent on doing homework (one decimal place)
5	Sleep	Number of hours per night sleeping (one decimal place)

Lesson 23: Using Sample Data to Compare the Means of
Two or More Populations

a. Ken decides to base his study on a random sample of 20 sixth graders and a random sample of 20 eleventh graders. The sixth graders have IDs 1–265, and the eleventh graders are numbered 266–440. Advise him on how to randomly sample 20 sixth graders and 20 eleventh graders from his data file.

Suppose that from a random number generator:

The random ID numbers for Ken's 20 sixth graders:
231 15 19 206 86 183 233 253 142 36 195 139 75 210 56 40 66 114 127 9

The random ID numbers for his 20 eleventh graders:
391 319 343 426 307 360 289 328 390 350 279 283 302 287 269 332 414 267 428 280

b. For each set, find the homework hours data from the population database that correspond to these randomly selected ID numbers.

c. On the same scale, draw dot plots for the two sample data sets.

Lesson 23:   Using Sample Data to Compare the Means of
                    Two or More Populations

EUREKA MATH

d. From looking at the dot plots, list some observations comparing the number of hours per week that sixth graders spend on doing homework and the number of hours per week that eleventh graders spend on doing homework.

e. Calculate the mean and MAD for each of the data sets. How many MADs separate the two sample means? (Use the larger MAD to make this calculation if the sample MADs are not the same.)

	Mean (hours)	MAD (hours)
Sixth Grade		
Eleventh Grade		

f. Ken recalled Linda suggesting that if the number of MADs is greater than or equal to 2, then it would be reasonable to think that the population of all sixth-grade students in his district and the population of all eleventh-grade students in his district have different means. What should Ken conclude based on his homework study?

Copy of the Excel student data file

ID Number	Texting	ReacTime	Homework	Sleep
1	99	0.33	9.0	8.2
2	69	0.39	8.6	7.5
3	138	0.36	6.1	8.7
4	100	0.40	7.9	7.8
5	116	0.28	5.1	8.8
6	112	0.38	6.5	7.9
7	79	0.35	6.5	8.8
8	111	0.41	8.8	8.5
9	115	0.49	8.4	8.4
10	82	0.43	8.7	8.8
11	136	0.46	7.2	8.4
12	112	0.51	8.3	9.0
13	101	0.42	7.0	8.8
14	89	0.38	5.6	8.3
15	120	0.35	7.2	8.2
16	144	0.36	3.9	8.8
17	131	0.26	9.0	8.9
18	126	0.39	7.0	8.5
19	118	0.37	9.2	8.7
20	83	0.34	7.4	8.6
21	120	0.20	4.5	8.7
22	114	0.38	6.0	8.6
23	90	0.25	7.0	8.4
24	116	0.36	5.8	8.4
25	108	0.36	8.9	8.1
26	89	0.31	8.4	8.8
27	124	0.44	6.3	8.3
28	121	0.32	5.2	8.0
29	104	0.30	6.7	8.1
30	110	0.39	7.8	8.1
31	119	0.36	8.5	8.0
32	113	0.40	5.3	9.4
33	106	0.36	5.7	8.6
34	119	0.33	5.9	8.4
35	129	0.38	6.2	9.0
36	95	0.44	7.9	8.3
37	126	0.41	7.2	8.6

38	106	0.26	7.1	8.5
39	116	0.34	4.9	8.4
40	107	0.35	9.3	8.1
41	108	0.48	8.1	8.6
42	97	0.40	7.1	8.8
43	97	0.27	4.2	8.3
44	100	0.24	6.2	8.9
45	123	0.50	8.1	8.6
46	94	0.39	5.2	8.3
47	87	0.37	8.0	8.3
48	93	0.42	9.7	8.1
49	117	0.39	7.9	8.3
50	94	0.36	6.9	8.9
51	124	0.29	8.1	8.4
52	116	0.44	4.9	8.2
53	137	0.25	9.1	8.3
54	123	0.30	3.8	8.7
55	122	0.21	6.6	8.8
56	92	0.41	7.6	8.6
57	101	0.36	8.5	8.2
58	111	0.34	6.5	8.7
59	126	0.31	5.6	8.6
60	81	0.33	7.3	8.4
61	118	0.35	8.4	8.3
62	113	0.37	7.7	8.4
63	114	0.49	6.9	8.6
64	124	0.34	8.5	8.1
65	90	0.48	6.6	8.7
66	99	0.39	6.5	8.5
67	155	0.40	6.5	9.0
68	77	0.45	4.9	8.3
69	79	0.23	7.7	8.6
70	91	0.43	6.7	8.9
71	107	0.42	6.9	8.6
72	112	0.39	6.3	8.6
73	147	0.34	7.8	8.3
74	126	0.52	9.2	8.9
75	106	0.27	6.7	8.0
76	86	0.21	6.1	8.4
77	111	0.29	7.4	8.0
78	118	0.41	5.2	8.8

Lesson 23: Using Sample Data to Compare the Means of Two or More Populations

EUREKA MATH

79	105	0.28	5.9	8.3
80	108	0.40	7.0	8.6
81	131	0.32	7.5	8.5
82	86	0.34	7.4	8.4
83	87	0.27	7.7	8.6
84	116	0.34	9.6	9.1
85	102	0.42	5.6	8.7
86	105	0.41	8.2	8.2
87	96	0.33	4.9	8.4
88	90	0.20	7.5	8.6
89	109	0.39	6.0	8.5
90	103	0.36	5.7	9.1
91	98	0.26	5.5	8.4
92	103	0.41	8.2	8.0
93	110	0.39	9.2	8.4
94	101	0.39	8.8	8.6
95	101	0.40	6.1	9.0
96	98	0.22	7.0	8.6
97	105	0.43	8.0	8.5
98	110	0.33	8.0	8.8
99	104	0.45	9.6	8.5
100	119	0.29	7.2	9.1
101	120	0.48	6.7	8.4
102	109	0.36	6.8	8.5
103	105	0.29	8.6	8.6
104	110	0.29	7.1	8.9
105	116	0.41	6.7	8.8
106	114	0.25	9.0	8.8
107	111	0.35	9.9	8.6
108	137	0.37	6.1	7.9
109	104	0.37	7.3	9.0
110	95	0.33	8.3	8.0
111	117	0.29	7.5	8.8
112	100	0.30	2.9	9.3
113	105	0.24	6.1	8.5
114	102	0.41	7.7	8.0
115	109	0.32	5.8	8.2
116	108	0.36	6.6	8.3
117	111	0.43	8.2	8.5
118	115	0.20	5.7	8.9
119	89	0.34	5.1	8.1

Lesson 23:   Using Sample Data to Compare the Means of
Two or More Populations

293

120	94	0.29	9.2	8.5
121	105	0.26	7.3	8.6
122	143	0.42	5.8	8.1
123	129	0.29	6.8	8.8
124	118	0.31	6.2	8.7
125	129	0.38	9.1	8.4
126	96	0.25	6.7	8.5
127	95	0.27	7.7	8.3
128	43	0.22	6.3	9.2
129	64	0.23	3.7	8.5
130	38	0.41	5.2	9.1
131	46	0.35	7.1	8.3
132	56	0.32	4.7	8.9
133	41	0.45	7.2	8.8
134	55	0.27	4.1	8.5
135	57	0.40	7.5	8.6
136	66	0.41	6.9	8.0
137	62	0.39	3.8	8.5
138	49	0.36	6.4	8.5
139	33	0.21	4.8	9.0
140	38	0.34	5.6	8.5
141	75	0.19	5.0	8.2
142	68	0.25	5.4	8.4
143	60	0.47	7.4	9.1
144	63	0.33	4.4	8.2
145	48	0.28	7.1	8.2
146	49	0.36	2.7	8.5
147	72	0.44	5.6	7.6
148	54	0.51	4.3	8.7
149	65	0.38	7.7	8.5
150	72	0.40	3.4	9.1
151	51	0.16	4.9	8.4
152	64	0.16	4.4	8.5
153	43	0.34	0.1	8.8
154	57	0.38	4.4	8.2
155	72	0.51	3.2	8.4
156	37	0.46	5.3	8.6
157	50	0.33	4.1	8.2
158	41	0.46	4.5	8.9
159	63	0.40	5.0	8.7
160	51	0.33	5.4	7.9

Lesson 23: Using Sample Data to Compare the Means of Two or More Populations

EUREKA MATH

161	57	0.51	4.9	8.6
162	51	0.24	1.7	8.4
163	73	0.32	5.6	8.6
164	51	0.37	4.0	8.5
165	52	0.36	5.8	8.3
166	52	0.34	4.6	8.1
167	63	0.34	4.1	8.1
168	76	0.30	6.1	8.2
169	56	0.40	5.7	8.5
170	47	0.33	5.0	8.2
171	44	0.41	5.0	8.3
172	60	0.33	7.7	8.4
173	36	0.39	6.5	8.8
174	52	0.30	5.4	8.2
175	53	0.27	5.6	8.2
176	60	0.35	6.0	8.6
177	48	0.43	3.6	8.6
178	63	0.49	0.2	8.2
179	76	0.42	5.9	8.9
180	58	0.34	7.3	8.3
181	51	0.43	6.4	8.7
182	38	0.33	4.9	8.5
183	46	0.17	4.7	8.3
184	53	0.34	6.4	8.7
185	60	0.38	6.1	8.7
186	71	0.23	6.9	8.2
187	54	0.41	2.9	8.3
188	61	0.44	5.8	8.4
189	62	0.35	3.9	8.9
190	55	0.15	4.8	8.0
191	57	0.22	4.1	8.2
192	43	0.41	7.5	8.5
193	51	0.34	2.4	8.6
194	34	0.55	3.5	8.4
195	38	0.43	7.1	8.8
196	49	0.38	3.5	8.3
197	57	0.30	3.6	8.5
198	53	0.37	5.2	9.1
199	51	0.36	5.1	8.2
200	59	0.38	3.6	8.7
201	35	0.44	4.0	8.0

202	73	0.32	3.0	8.3
203	68	0.37	2.7	8.4
204	31	0.36	4.6	8.6
205	40	0.33	9.0	8.3
206	60	0.36	6.6	8.5
207	66	0.44	4.2	8.5
208	47	0.22	4.5	8.7
209	56	0.30	4.8	8.6
210	72	0.36	2.9	8.8
211	68	0.50	6.6	8.3
212	45	0.37	7.3	8.5
213	58	0.17	4.9	9.0
214	64	0.34	3.2	8.6
215	66	0.34	2.5	8.4
216	49	0.29	5.0	8.3
217	83	0.39	2.5	8.8
218	73	0.33	3.6	8.4
219	52	0.34	3.3	8.8
220	56	0.28	8.8	8.7
221	58	0.32	5.6	8.3
222	53	0.40	5.9	8.1
223	50	0.23	4.4	8.4
224	43	0.34	3.9	8.7
225	50	0.39	4.4	8.0
226	44	0.31	4.4	8.4
227	59	0.36	6.0	9.1
228	41	0.35	3.2	8.4
229	53	0.29	6.6	8.7
230	49	0.37	5.7	8.3
231	42	0.22	8.5	8.6
232	48	0.34	3.9	8.2
233	60	0.31	6.1	8.8
234	56	0.50	2.6	8.5
235	43	0.25	5.3	8.9
236	67	0.32	6.1	8.8
237	43	0.24	8.6	8.8
238	41	0.46	5.1	8.7
239	66	0.45	4.9	8.3
240	44	0.52	4.1	8.7
241	70	0.43	6.6	8.8
242	63	0.38	7.9	8.4

Lesson 23:   Using Sample Data to Compare the Means of
Two or More Populations

EUREKA
MATH®

243	47	0.24	3.9	8.3
244	52	0.38	5.4	8.8
245	49	0.47	4.2	8.4
246	45	0.31	8.1	8.8
247	46	0.37	1.9	8.3
248	19	0.31	6.5	8.3
249	63	0.40	6.1	8.5
250	64	0.35	5.8	8.1
251	63	0.34	6.7	8.5
252	68	0.46	6.9	8.5
253	48	0.43	8.6	8.7
254	43	0.38	4.4	8.3
255	50	0.32	4.6	8.7
256	76	0.31	4.0	8.3
257	64	0.39	5.7	8.6
258	38	0.29	6.4	8.0
259	90	0.30	7.0	8.6
260	37	0.39	4.8	8.8
261	58	0.37	6.5	8.0
262	42	0.27	4.5	8.6
263	58	0.37	6.0	8.3
264	42	0.42	7.2	8.8
265	66	0.33	12.6	8.8
266	116	0.44	8.7	7.5
267	76	0.43	9.5	6.9
268	125	0.46	9.9	6.8
269	128	0.41	9.8	6.6
270	128	0.37	11.3	7.1
271	125	0.44	6.7	7.9
272	80	0.49	10.6	7.1
273	110	0.48	9.9	7.2
274	135	0.41	9.8	7.8
275	136	0.45	8.9	7.2
276	142	0.43	10.2	8.0
277	120	0.48	10.2	7.5
278	109	0.43	10.1	7.1
279	109	0.50	10.9	7.5
280	111	0.35	11.8	7.4
281	101	0.49	8.5	7.8
282	98	0.50	11.6	7.2
283	91	0.56	10.0	7.3

284	151	0.50	7.7	6.7
285	82	0.48	14.0	7.5
286	107	0.48	9.5	7.5
287	83	0.40	12.0	7.2
288	91	0.40	9.2	7.9
289	127	0.40	9.1	7.6
290	115	0.42	11.6	6.8
291	118	0.40	9.8	7.3
292	89	0.42	10.8	7.0
293	100	0.46	11.6	7.3
294	97	0.39	8.5	7.8
295	110	0.36	11.1	7.7
296	88	0.40	9.0	6.7
297	103	0.47	11.7	6.7
298	82	0.49	10.7	7.5
299	87	0.41	8.1	7.4
300	130	0.39	9.8	7.6
301	116	0.42	9.6	7.6
302	96	0.42	11.8	7.1
303	122	0.39	7.9	7.1
304	70	0.38	11.1	7.4
305	116	0.47	8.8	7.3
306	122	0.48	9.0	7.0
307	109	0.45	10.0	7.3
308	114	0.50	10.1	7.3
309	62	0.47	11.4	7.3
310	120	0.51	9.5	6.3
311	130	0.38	10.5	7.7
312	92	0.47	11.8	7.3
313	81	0.55	7.9	7.3
314	82	0.51	10.1	7.7
315	102	0.48	10.9	6.5
316	113	0.43	10.2	7.9
317	119	0.43	8.0	6.8
318	108	0.48	8.9	7.0
319	130	0.53	8.3	7.3
320	111	0.50	9.9	6.6
321	132	0.50	11.5	6.8
322	110	0.47	10.8	7.1
323	95	0.49	10.4	7.5
324	137	0.29	9.8	7.5

Lesson 23:   Using Sample Data to Compare the Means of
Two or More Populations

EUREKA
MATH

325	98	0.53	11.5	7.0
326	124	0.55	10.2	6.6
327	146	0.36	10.2	7.5
328	126	0.51	10.6	6.5
329	124	0.53	9.4	7.6
330	99	0.47	8.7	7.7
331	100	0.51	9.5	7.9
332	101	0.45	9.5	7.1
333	113	0.37	9.4	7.8
334	139	0.42	8.9	7.1
335	105	0.38	8.7	7.4
336	113	0.45	10.7	7.3
337	104	0.45	9.6	7.2
338	117	0.48	10.3	7.3
339	132	0.43	10.9	7.7
340	100	0.44	11.8	6.8
341	109	0.40	8.1	7.2
342	95	0.39	9.7	7.4
343	139	0.39	9.8	7.7
344	140	0.47	8.9	7.3
345	110	0.48	12.1	7.2
346	97	0.56	11.5	8.2
347	98	0.49	11.2	6.9
348	146	0.44	10.0	7.2
349	92	0.47	12.0	6.5
350	128	0.43	10.8	7.7
351	156	0.50	11.4	6.3
352	134	0.39	9.1	8.2
353	110	0.44	7.6	6.6
354	104	0.45	12.4	7.5
355	98	0.54	11.0	7.1
356	120	0.50	10.5	7.3
357	140	0.50	10.6	6.9
358	130	0.53	10.7	7.4
359	115	0.45	10.1	7.1
360	159	0.41	10.7	7.5
361	114	0.43	9.9	6.9
362	128	0.46	9.3	7.0
363	96	0.49	7.6	7.5
364	61	0.49	12.0	6.7
365	60	0.46	8.2	7.6

366	51	0.50	7.8	7.6
367	61	0.49	7.9	7.1
368	46	0.57	7.5	6.5
369	60	0.44	8.0	7.7
370	53	0.36	12.5	7.1
371	55	0.45	10.7	7.3
372	59	0.38	9.0	7.0
373	61	0.38	9.3	6.9
374	69	0.57	10.4	7.4
375	63	0.51	10.6	7.0
376	62	0.48	12.8	7.1
377	57	0.49	7.8	7.4
378	70	0.40	11.2	6.9
379	31	0.46	9.2	6.6
380	70	0.41	10.8	6.8
381	66	0.39	10.9	7.8
382	62	0.51	9.8	6.3
383	75	0.50	9.6	7.2
384	58	0.34	9.1	7.2
385	50	0.47	11.3	7.3
386	73	0.44	9.1	7.4
387	61	0.37	10.8	7.2
388	48	0.48	8.1	6.8
389	54	0.52	12.4	7.6
390	63	0.52	9.4	7.1
391	69	0.35	13.2	7.1
392	71	0.39	12.0	7.6
393	44	0.40	10.6	7.4
394	60	0.42	11.8	6.8
395	79	0.37	9.4	7.9
396	38	0.50	9.9	7.3
397	80	0.57	11.0	7.0
398	54	0.46	8.8	6.9
399	74	0.44	10.8	7.6
400	37	0.40	9.3	7.8
401	69	0.47	9.8	7.1
402	54	0.47	9.6	7.3
403	68	0.42	10.1	8.1
404	49	0.56	8.9	7.2
405	55	0.45	6.1	7.2
406	64	0.43	10.2	6.9

Lesson 23:   Using Sample Data to Compare the Means of
Two or More Populations

EUREKA
MATH®

407	83	0.41	7.3	6.6
408	36	0.46	11.5	7.3
409	44	0.43	11.0	6.7
410	65	0.44	11.1	7.0
411	77	0.39	12.1	7.7
412	33	0.44	6.9	7.1
413	45	0.47	8.2	6.9
414	70	0.53	7.3	7.2
415	77	0.44	8.9	7.2
416	53	0.46	9.2	6.8
417	60	0.49	11.0	7.4
418	86	0.44	5.8	7.8
419	49	0.55	8.4	7.2
420	50	0.45	12.3	6.5
421	64	0.41	10.7	7.2
422	57	0.45	7.0	7.1
423	56	0.40	12.1	6.5
424	41	0.45	12.7	7.2
425	50	0.50	8.3	6.8
426	63	0.45	11.6	7.4
427	44	0.43	7.7	7.1
428	51	0.42	10.3	7.5
429	51	0.50	8.7	7.1
430	54	0.43	8.4	7.2
431	45	0.44	7.0	6.9
432	65	0.46	10.5	7.5
433	60	0.45	7.4	7.1
434	52	0.42	4.1	7.1
435	50	0.49	11.2	6.9
436	61	0.52	10.7	6.7
437	42	0.43	9.2	6.8
438	42	0.50	11.4	6.8
439	66	0.47	7.9	7.2
440	65	0.43	9.2	7.1

Lesson 23:   Using Sample Data to Compare the Means of
Two or More Populations

Name _____ Date _____

1. Do eleventh-grade males text more per day than eleventh-grade females do? To answer this question, two randomly selected samples were obtained from the Excel data file used in this lesson. Indicate how 20 randomly selected eleventh-grade females would be chosen for this study. Indicate how 20 randomly selected eleventh-grade males would be chosen.

2. Two randomly selected samples (one of eleventh-grade females and one of eleventh-grade males) were obtained from the database. The results are indicated below:

	Mean Number of Minutes per Day Texting	MAD (minutes)
Eleventh-Grade Females	102.55	1.31
Eleventh-Grade Males	100.32	1.12

Is there a meaningful difference in the number of minutes per day that eleventh-grade females and males text? Explain your answer.

Principal MacDonald wanted to determine if sixth graders or eighth graders were absent more often. The table below shows the number of absences 12 students in each grade had throughout the year.

Sixth Grade	4	0	6	10	8	7	3	2	4	7	6	5
Eighth Grade	0	8	12	4	7	6	9	10	1	3	2	2

1. On the same scale, draw dot plots for the two sample data sets.

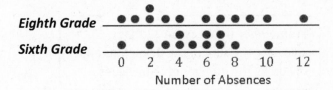

2. Looking at the dot plots, list some observations comparing the number of absences for sixth graders and the number of absences for eighth graders.

    The dot plots look similar. The variability is slightly larger for eighth grade students than for sixth grade students. However, both data distributions look like they have means close to each other.

    > Although answers may vary a little, it is important for students to notice the dot plots are similar.

An additional explanation for how to calculate this information can be found in Lesson 22.

3. Calculate the mean and MAD for each of the data sets. Round to the nearest hundredth if necessary.

	Mean (days)	MAD (days)
Sixth Grade	5.17	2.17
Eighth Grade	5.33	3.33

I add all the data values and divide by the number of data values.

I remember from Lesson 22 that I calculate the sum of the deviations and divide by the number of data values.

4. How many MADs separate the two sample means?

$$\frac{5.33 - 5.17}{3.33} \approx 0.05$$

I calculate the difference between the means and divide by the largest MAD.

5. What can you say about the average number of absences for all sixth graders in the population compared to the average number of absences for all eighth graders in the population?

Since the number of MADs that separate the means is approximately 0.05, we can assume sixth graders and eighth graders miss about the same amount of school.

In order to conclude that students in one grade miss more school than another grade, the separation between the means needs to be significant.

Lesson 23:   Using Sample Data to Compare the Means of Two or More Populations

EUREKA MATH®

1. Based on Ken's population database, compare the amount of sleep that sixth-grade females get on average to the amount of sleep that eleventh-grade females get on average.

    Find the data for 15 sixth-grade females based on the following random ID numbers:

    65 1 67 101 106 87 85 95 120 4 64 74 102 31 128

    Find the data for 15 eleventh-grade females based on the following random ID numbers:

    348 313 297 351 294 343 275 354 311 328 274 305 288 267 301

2. On the same scale, draw dot plots for the two sample data sets.

3. Looking at the dot plots, list some observations comparing the number of hours per night that sixth graders spend sleeping and the number of hours per night that eleventh graders spend sleeping.

4. Calculate the mean and MAD for each of the data sets. How many MADs separate the two sample means? (Use the larger MAD to make this calculation if the sample MADs are not the same.)

	Mean (hours)	MAD (hours)
Sixth-Grade Females		
Eleventh-Grade Females		

5. Recall that if the number of MADs in the difference of two sample means is greater than or equal to 2, then it would be reasonable to think that the population means are different. Using this guideline, what can you say about the average number of hours of sleep per night for all sixth-grade females in the population compared to all eleventh-grade females in the population?

Credits

Great Minds® has made every effort to obtain permission for the reprinting of all copyrighted material. If any owner of copyrighted material is not acknowledged herein, please contact Great Minds for proper acknowledgment in all future editions and reprints of this module.